Paul B. Sawyn

Jan 15— 1938

THE BLUE BIRD

THE BLUE BIRD

A Fairy Play in Six Acts

BY
MAURICE MAETERLINCK

Translated by
ALEXANDER TEIXEIRA DE MATTOS

NEW YORK
DODD, MEAD AND COMPANY
1937

CHARACTERS

TYLTYL	THE WOLF
MYTYL	THE PIG
LIGHT	THE OX
THE FAIRY BÉRYLUNE	THE COW
NEIGHBOUR BERLINGOT	THE BULL
DADDY TYL	THE SHEEP
MUMMY TYL	THE COCK
GAFFER TYL	THE RABBIT
GRANNY TYL	THE HORSE
TYLTYL'S BROTHERS	THE ASS
AND SISTERS	THE OAK
TIME	THE ELM
NIGHT	THE BEECH

Dead (bracketing GAFFER TYL, GRANNY TYL, TYLTYL'S BROTHERS AND SISTERS)

NEIGHBOUR BERLINGOT'S LITTLE DAUGHTER	THE LIME-TREE
TYLÔ, THE DOG	THE FIR-TREE
TYLETTE, THE CAT	THE CYPRESS
BREAD	THE BIRCH
SUGAR	THE CHESTNUT-TREE
FIRE	THE IVY
WATER	THE POPLAR
MILK	THE WILLOW

STARS, SICKNESSES, SHADES, LUXURIES, HAPPINESSES, JOYS, ETC.

5

TRANSLATOR'S NOTE

A NEW act appears for the first time in this edition and is inserted as Act IV—*The Palace of Happiness*. It has been specially written for the Christmas revival of *The Blue Bird* at the Haymarket Theatre, where it will take the place of the Forest Scene (Act III., Scene 2). In the printed version, however, the Forest Scene is retained; and in this and all later editions the play will consist of six acts instead of five.

ALEXANDER TEIXEIRA DE MATTOS.

CHELSEA, 14 *November*, 1910.

COSTUMES

TYLTYL wears the dress of Hop o' my Thumb in Perrault's Tales. Scarlet knickerbockers, pale-blue jacket, white stockings, tan shoes.

MYTYL is dressed like Gretel or Little Red Riding-hood.

LIGHT.—The "moon-coloured" dress in Perrault's *Peau d'âne;* that is to say, pale gold shot with silver, shimmering gauzes, forming a sort of rays, etc. Neo-Grecian or Anglo-Grecian (*à la* Walter Crane) or even more or less Empire style: a high waist, bare arms, etc. Head-dress: a sort of diadem or even a light crown.

THE FAIRY BÉRYLUNE and NEIGHBOUR BERLINGOT.—The traditional dress of the poor women in fairy-tales. If desired, the transformation of the Fairy into a princess in Act I may be omitted.

7

DADDY TYL, MUMMY TYL, GAFFER TYL and GRANNY TYL.—The traditional costume of the German wood-cutters and peasants in Grimm's Tales.

TYLTYL'S BROTHERS AND SISTERS.—Different forms of the Hop-o'-my-Thumb costume.

TIME.—Traditional dress of Time: a wide black or dark-blue cloak, a streaming white beard, scythe and hour-glass.

NIGHT.—Ample black garments, covered with mysterious stars and "shot" with reddish-brown reflections. Veils, dark poppies, etc.

THE NEIGHBOUR'S LITTLE GIRL.—Bright fair hair; a long white frock.

THE DOG.—Red dress-coat, white breeches, top-boots, a shiny hat. The costume suggests that of John Bull.

THE CAT.—The costume of Puss in Boots: powdered wig, three-cornered hat, violet or sky-blue coat, dress-sword, etc.

N.B.—The heads of the DOG and the CAT should be only discreetly animalised.

THE LUXURIES.—Before the transformation: wide, heavy mantles in red and yellow brocade; enormous fat jewels, etc. After the transformation: chocolate or coffee-coloured tights, giving the impression of unadorned dancing-jacks.

THE HAPPINESSES OF THE HOME.—Dresses of various colours, or, if preferred, costumes of peasants, shepherds, wood-cutters and so on, but idealised and interpreted fairy-fashion.

THE GREAT JOYS.—As stated in the text, shimmering dresses in soft and subtle shades: rose-awakening, water's-smile, amber-dew, blue-of-dawn, etc.

MATERNAL LOVE.—Dress very similar to the dress worn by Light, that is to say, supple and almost transparent veils, as of a Greek statue, and, in so far as possible, white. Pearls and other stones as rich and numerous as may be desired, provided that they do not break the pure and candid harmony of the whole.

9

BREAD.—A rich pasha's dress. An ample crimson silk or velvet gown. A huge turban. A scimitar. An enormous stomach, red and puffed-out cheeks.

SUGAR.—A silk gown, cut like that of a eunuch in a seraglio, half blue and half white, to suggest the paper wrapper of a sugar-loaf. Eunuch's head-dress.

FIRE.—Red tights, a vermilion cloak with changing reflections, lined with gold. An aigrette of iridescent flames.

WATER.—A pale-blue or bluish-green dress, with transparent reflections and effects of rippling or trickling gauze. Neo-Grecian or Anglo-Grecian style, but fuller and more voluminous than that of LIGHT. Head-dress of aquatic flowers and seaweed.

THE ANIMALS.—Popular or peasant costumes.

THE TREES.—Dresses of different shades of green or the colour of the trunks of trees. Distinctive attributes in the shape of leaves or branches by which they can be recognised.

SCENES

The Blue Bird

ACT I

The Wood-cutter's Cottage

The stage represents the interior of a wood-cutter's cottage, simple and rustic in appearance, but in no way poverty-stricken. A recessed fireplace containing the dying embers of a wood-fire. Kitchen utensils, a cupboard, a bread-pan, a grandfather's clock, a spinning-wheel, a water-tap, etc. On a table, a lighted lamp. At the foot of the cupboard, on either side, a DOG and a CAT lie sleeping, rolled up, each with his nose in his tail. Between them stands a large blue-and-white sugar-loaf. On the wall hangs a round cage containing a turtle-dove. At the back, two windows, with closed inside shutters. Under one of the windows, a stool. On the left is the front door, with a

13

big latch to it. On the right, another door. A ladder leads up to a loft. On the right also are two little children's cots, at the head of which are two chairs, with clothes carefully folded on them. When the curtain rises, TYLTYL *and* MYTYL *are sound asleep in their cots.* MUMMY TYL *tucks them in, leans over them, watches them for a moment as they sleep and beckons to* DADDY TYL, *who thrusts his head through the half-open door.* MUMMY TYL *lays a finger on her lips, to impose silence upon him, and then goes out to the right, on tiptoe, after first putting out the lamp. The scene remains in darkness for a moment. Then a light, gradually increasing in intensity, filters in through the shutters. The lamp on the table lights again of itself, but its light is of a different colour than when* MUMMY TYL *extinguished it. The two* CHILDREN *appear to wake and sit up in bed.*

14

TYLTYL

Mytyl?

MYTYL

Tyltyl?

TYLTYL

Are you asleep?

MYTYL

Are you? . . .

TYLTYL

No; how can I be asleep when I'm talking
to you?

MYTYL

Say, is this Christmas Day? . . .

TYLTYL

Not yet; not till to-morrow. But Father
Christmas won't bring us anything
this year. . . .

MYTYL

Why not?

TYLTYL

I heard mummy say that she couldn't go
to town to tell him. . . . But he will
come next year. . . .

MYTYL

Is next year far off? . . .

TYLTYL

A good long while. . . . But he will come
to the rich children to-night. . . .

MYTYL

Really? . . .

TYLTYL

Hullo! . . . Mummy's forgotten to
put out the lamp! . . . I've an
idea! . . .

MYTYL

What? . . .

TYLTYL

Let's get up. . . .

MYTYL

But we mustn't. . . .

TYLTYL

Why, there's no one about. . . . Do you
see the shutters? . . .

MYTYL

Oh, how bright they are! . . .

TYLTYL

It's the lights of the party.

MYTYL

What party? . . .

The Blue Bird

TYLTYL

The rich children opposite. It's the Christmas-tree. Let's open the shutters. . . .

MYTYL

Can we? . . .

TYLTYL

Of course; there's no one to stop us. . . . Do you hear the music? . . . Let us get up. . . .

> (*The two* CHILDREN *get up, run to one of the windows, climb on to the stool and throw back the shutters. A bright light fills the room. The* CHILDREN *look out greedily.*)

TYLTYL

We can see everything! . . .

MYTYL (*who can hardly find room on the stool*)

I can't. . . .

TYLTYL

It's snowing! . . . There's two carriages,
with six horses each! . . .

MYTYL

There are twelve little boys getting
out! . . .

TYLTYL

How silly you are! . . . They're little
girls. . . .

MYTYL

They've got knickerbockers. . . .

TYLTYL

What do you know? . . . Don't push
so! . . .

MYTYL

I never touched you.

TYLTYL (*who is taking up the whole stool*)

You're taking up all the room. . . .

MYTYL

Why, I have no room at all! . . .

TYLTYL

Do be quiet! I see the tree! . . .

MYTYL

What tree? . . .

18

TYLTYL

Why, the Christmas-tree! . . . You're
looking at the wall! . . .

MYTYL

I'm looking at the wall because I've got no
room. . . .

TYLTYL (*giving her a miserly little place
on the stool*)

There! . . . Will that do? . . . Now
you're better off than I! . . . I say,
what lots and lots of lights! . . .

MYTYL

What are those people doing who are mak-
such a noise? . . .

TYLTYL

They're the musicians.

MYTYL

Are they angry? . . .

TYLTYL

No; but it's hard work.

MYTYL

Another carriage with white horses!

TYLTYL

Be quiet! . . . And look! . . .

The Blue Bird

MYTYL

What are those gold things there, hanging from the branches?

TYLTYL

Why, toys, to be sure! . . . Swords, guns, soldiers, cannons. . . .

MYTYL

And dolls; say, are there any dolls? . . .

TYLTYL

Dolls? . . . That's too silly; there's no fun in dolls. . . .

MYTYL

And what's that all round the table? . . .

TYLTYL

Cakes and fruit and tarts. . . .

MYTYL

I had some once when I was little. . . .

TYLTYL

So did I; it's nicer than bread, but they don't give you enough. . . .

MYTYL

They've got plenty over there. . . . The whole table's full. . . . Are they going to eat them? . . .

TYLTYL

Of course; what else would they do with them? . . .

MYTYL

Why don't they eat them at once? . . .

TYLTYL

Because they're not hungry. . . .

MYTYL (*stupefied with astonishment*)

Not hungry? . . . Why not? . . .

TYLTYL

Well, they eat whenever they want to. . . .

MYTYL (*incredulously*)

Every day? . . .

TYLTYL

They say so. . . .

MYTYL

Will they eat them all? . . . Will they give any away? . . .

TYLTYL

To whom? . . .

MYTYL

To us. . . .

TYLTYL

They don't know us. . . .

MYTYL

Suppose we asked them. . . .

TYLTYL

We mustn't.

MYTYL

Why not? . . .

TYLTYL

Because it's not right.

MYTYL (*clapping her hands*)

Oh, how pretty they are! . . .

TYLTYL (*rapturously*)

And how they're laughing and laughing! . . .

MYTYL

And the little ones dancing! . . .

TYLTYL

Yes, yes; let's dance too! . . . (*They stamp their feet for joy on the stool.*)

MYTYL

Oh, what fun! . . .

TYLTYL

They're getting the cakes! . . . They can touch them! . . . They're eating, they're eating, they're eating! . . .

22

The Blue Bird

MYTYL

The tiny ones, too! . . . They've got two,
three, four apiece! . . .

TYLTYL (*drunk with delight*)

Oh, how lovely! . . . Oh, how lovely, how
lovely! . . .

MYTYL (*counting imaginary cakes*)

I've got twelve! . . .

TYLTYL

And I four times twelve! . . . But I'll give
you some. . . .

(*A knock at the door of the cottage*).

TYLTYL (*suddenly quieted and frightened*)

What's that? . . .

MYTYL (*scared*)

It's Daddy! . . .

(*As they hesitate before opening
the door, the big latch is
seen to rise of itself, with a
grating noise; the door half
opens to admit a little old
woman dressed in green
with a red hood on her*

23

*head. She is humpbacked
and lame and near-sighted;
her nose and chin meet; and
she walks bent on a stick.
She is obviously a fairy.)*

THE FAIRY

Have you the grass here that sings or the
bird that is blue? . . .

TYLTYL

We have some grass, but it can't sing. . . .

MYTYL

Tyltyl has a bird.

TYLTYL

But I can't give it away. . . .

THE FAIRY

Why not? . . .

TYLTYL

Because it's mine.

THE FAIRY

That's a reason, no doubt. Where is the
bird? . . .

TYLTYL (*pointing to the cage*)

In the cage. . . .

THE FAIRY (*putting on her glasses to ex-
amine the bird*)

The Blue Bird

I don't want it; it's not blue enough. You
will have to go and find me the one I
want.

TYLTYL

But I don't know where it is. . . .

THE FAIRY

No more do I. That's why you must look
for it. I can do without the grass that
sings, at a pinch; but I must absolutely
have the blue bird. It's for my little
girl, who is very ill.

TYLTYL

What's the matter with her? . . .

THE FAIRY

We don't quite know; she wants to be
happy. . . .

TYLTYL

Really? . . .

THE FAIRY

Do you know who I am? . . .

TYLTYL

You're rather like our neighbour, Madame
Berlingot. . . .

THE FAIRY (*growing suddenly angry*)

Not a bit! . . . There's not the least like-

25

ness! . . . This is intolerable! . . .
I am the Fairy Bérylune. . . .

TYLTYL

Oh! Very well. . . .

THE FAIRY

You will have to start at once.

TYLTYL

Are you coming with us?

THE FAIRY

I can't, because I put on the soup this morning and it always boils over if I leave
it for more than hour. . . . (*Pointing successively to the ceiling, the
chimney and the window*) Will you
go out this way, or that way, or that
way? . . .

TYLTYL (*pointing timidly to the door*)

I would rather go out that way. . . .

THE FAIRY (*growing suddenly angry
again*)

That's quite impossible; and it's a shocking
habit! . . . (*Pointing to the window*)
We'll go out this way. . . . Well?
. . . What are you waiting for? . . .
Get dressed at once. . . . (*The* CHIL-

DREN *do as they are told and dress quickly*.) I'll help Mytyl. . . .

TYLTYL

We have no shoes. . . .

THE FAIRY

That doesn't matter. I will give you a little magic hat. Where are your father and mother? . . .

TYLTYL (*pointing to the door on the right*)

They're asleep in there. . . .

THE FAIRY

And your grandpapa and grandmamma? . . .

TYLTYL

They're dead. . . .

THE FAIRY

And your little brothers and sisters. . . . Have you any? . . .

TYLTYL

Oh, yes; three little brothers. . . .

MYTYL

And four little sisters. . . .

THE FAIRY

Where are they? . . .

27

TYLTYL

They are dead, too. . . .

THE FAIRY

Would you like to see them again? . . .

TYLTYL

Oh, yes! . . . At once! . . . Show them to us! . . .

THE FAIRY

I haven't got them in my pocket. . . . But this is very lucky; you will see them when you go through the Land of Memory. . . . It's on the way to the Blue Bird, just on the left, past the third turning. . . . What were you doing when I knocked? . . .

TYLTYL

We were playing at eating cakes? . . .

THE FAIRY

Have you any cakes? . . . Where are they? . . .

TYLTYL

In the house of the rich children. . . . Come and look, it's so lovely. (*He drags the* FAIRY *to the window.*)

THE FAIRY (*at the window*)

28

But it's the others who are eating them! . . .

TYLTYL

Yes; but we can see them eat. . . .

THE FAIRY

Aren't you cross with them? . . .

TYLTYL

What for? . . .

THE FAIRY

For eating all the cakes. . . . I think it's very wrong of them not to give you some. . . .

TYLTYL

Not at all; they're rich. . . . I say, isn't it beautiful over there? . . .

THE FAIRY

It's no more beautiful there than here.

TYLTYL

Ugh! . . . It's darker here and smaller and there are no cakes. . . .

THE FAIRY

It's exactly the same, only you can't see. . . .

TYLTYL

Yes, I can; and I have very good eyes. I can see the time on the church clock and daddy can't . . .

The Blue Bird

THE FAIRY (*suddenly angry*)

I tell you that you can't see! . . . How do
you see me? . . . What do I look
like? . . . (*An awkward silence from*
TYLTYL.) Well, answer me, will
you? I want to know if you can see!
. . . Am I pretty or ugly? . . .
(*The silence grows more and more
uncomfortable.*) Won't you answer?
. . . Am I young or old? . . . Are
my cheeks pink or yellow? . . .
Perhaps you'll say I have a hump? . . .

TYLTYL (*in a conciliatory tone*)

No, no; it's not a big one. . . .

THE FAIRY

Oh, yes, to look at you, any one would think
it enormous. . . . Have I a hook nose
and have I lost one of my eyes? . . .

TYLTYL

Oh, no, I don't say that. . . . Who put it
out? . . .

THE FAIRY (*growing more and more
irritated*).

But it's not out! . . . You wretched, impu-
dent boy! . . . It's much finer than

30

the other; it's bigger and brighter and blue as the sky. . . . And my hair, do you see that? . . . It's fair as the corn in the fields, it's like virgin gold! . . . And I've such heaps and heaps of it that it weighs my head down. . . . It escapes on every side. . . . Do you see it on my hands? (*She holds out two lean wisps of grey hair.*)

TYLTYL

Yes, I see a little. . . .

THE FAIRY (*indignantly*)

A little! . . . Sheaves! Armfuls! Clusters! Waves of gold! . . . I know there are people who say that they don't see any; but you're not one of those wicked, blind people, I should hope? . . .

TYLTYL

Oh, no; I can see all that isn't hidden. . . .

THE FAIRY

But you ought to see the rest with as little doubt! . . . Human beings are very odd! . . . Since the death of the fairies, they see nothing at all and they

31

never suspect it. . . . Luckily, I always carry with me all that is wanted to give new light to dimmed eyes. . . . What am I taking out of my bag? . . .

TYLTYL

Oh, what a dear little green hat! . . . What's that shining in the cockade? . . .

THE FAIRY

That's the big diamond that makes people see. . . .

TYLTYL

Really? . . .

THE FAIRY

Yes; when you've got the hat on your head, you turn the diamond a little; from right to left, for instance, like this; do you see? . . . Then it presses a bump which nobody knows of and which opens your eyes. . . .

TYLTYL

Doesn't it hurt? . . .

THE FAIRY

On the contrary, it's enchanted. . . . You

at once see even the inside of things: the soul of bread, of wine, of pepper, for instance. . . .

MYTYL

Can you see the soul of sugar, too? . . .

THE FAIRY (*suddenly cross*)

Of course you can! . . . I hate unnecessary questions. . . . The soul of sugar is no more interesting than the soul of pepper. . . . There, I give you all I have to help you in your search for the Blue Bird. I know that the flying carpet or the ring which makes its wearer invisible would be more useful to you. . . . But I have lost the key of the cupboard in which I locked them. . . . Oh, I was almost forgetting! . . . (*Pointing to the diamond*) When you hold it like this, do you see? . . . One little turn more and you behold the past. . . . Another little turn and you behold the future. . . . It's curious and practical and it's quite noiseless. . . .

33

TYLTYL

Daddy will take it from me. . . .

THE FAIRY

He won't see it; no one can see it as long
as it's on your head. . . . Will you
try it? . . . (*She puts the little green
hat on* TYLTYL's *head.*) Now, turn
the diamond. . . . One turn and
then. . . .

(TYLTYL *has no sooner turned
the diamond than a sudden
and wonderful change comes
over everything. The old
FAIRY alters then and there
into a princess of marvellous
beauty; the flints of which
the cottage walls are built
light up, turn blue as sap-
phires, become transparent
and gleam and sparkle like
the most precious stones.
The humble furniture takes
life and becomes resplen-
dent; the deal table assumes
as grave and noble an air as*

34

a table made of marble; the
face of the clock winks its
eye and smiles genially,
while the door that con-
tains the pendulum opens
and releases the Hours,
which, holding one another
by the hand and laughing
merrily, begin to dance to
the sound of delicious music.

TYLTYL (*displaying a legitimate bewilder-*
ment and pointing to the Hours)
Who are all those pretty ladies? . . .

THE FAIRY
Don't be afraid; they are the hours of your
life and they are glad to be free and
visible for a moment. . . .

TYLTYL
And why are the walls so bright? . . . Are
they made of sugar or of precious
stones? . . .

THE FAIRY
All stones are alike, all stones are precious;
but man sees only a few of them. . . .

35

*(While they are speaking, the
scene of enchantment con-
tinues and is completed.
The souls of the Quartern-
loaves, in the form of
little men in crust-coloured
tights, flurried and all powdered with flour, scramble
out of the bread-pan and
frisk round the table, where
they are caught up by* FIRE,
*who, springing from the
hearth in yellow and ver-
milion tights, writhes with
laughter as he chases the
loaves.)*

TYLTYL

Who are those ugly little men? . . .

THE FAIRY

Oh, they're nothing; they are merely the
souls of the Quartern-loaves, who are
taking advantage of the reign of truth
to leave the pan in which they were too
tightly packed. . . .

36

TYLTYL

And the big red fellow, with the nasty
    smell? . . .

THE FAIRY

Hush! . . . Don't speak too loud; that's
    Fire. . . . He's dangerous.

(*This dialogue does not interrupt
    the enchantment. The* DOG
    and the CAT, *lying rolled up
    at the foot of the cupboard,
    utter a loud and simultane-
    ous cry and disappear down
    a trap; and in their places
    rise two persons, one of
    whom has the face of a bull-
    dog, the other that of a tom-
    cat. Forthwith, the little
    man with the bull-dog
    face, whom we will hence-
    forward call the* DOG,
    rushes upon TYLTYL, *kisses
    him violently and over-
    whelms him with noisy and
    impetuous caresses; while
    the little man with the face*

37

*of a tom-cat, whom we will
simply call the* CAT, *combs
his hair, washes his hands
and strokes his whiskers
before going up to* MYTYL.)

THE DOG (*yelling, jumping about, knocking up against everything, unbearable*).
My little god! . . . Good-morning, good-
morning, my dear little god! . . . At
last, at last we can talk! . . . I had
so much to tell you! . . . Bark and
wag my tail as I might, you never un-
derstood! . . . But now! . . . Good-
morning, good-morning! . . . I
love you! . . . Shall I do some of my
tricks? . . . Shall I beg? . . . Would
you like to see me walk on my front
paws or dance on my hind-legs? . . .

TYLTYL (*to the* FAIRY)
Who is this gentleman with the dog's
head? . . .

THE FAIRY
Don't you see? It's the soul of TYLÔ,
whom you have set free. . . .

38

The Blue Bird

THE CAT (*going up to* MYTYL *and putting out his hand to her, with much ceremony and circumspection*)

Good-morning, Miss. . . .. How well you look this morning! . . .

MYTYL

Good-morning, sir. . . . (*To the* FAIRY) Who is it? . . .

THE FAIRY

Why, don't you see? Its the soul of Tylette offering you his hand. . . . Kiss him. . . .

THE DOG (*hustling the* CAT)

Me, too! . . . I've kissed the little god! . . . I've kissed the little girl! . . . I've kissed everybody! . . . Oh, grand! . . . What fun we shall have! . . . I'm going to frighten Tylette! Bow, wow, wow! . . .

THE CAT

Sir, I don't know you. . . .

THE FAIRY (*threatening the* DOG *with her stick*)

Keep still, will you, or else you'll go back into silence until the end of time. . . .

39

The Blue Bird

(Meanwhile, the enchantment has pursued its course: the spinning-wheel has begun to turn madly in its corner and to spin brilliant rays of light; the tap, in another corner, begins to sing in a very high voice and, turning into a luminous fountain, floods the sink with sheets of pearls and emeralds, through which darts the soul of WATER, *like a young girl, streaming, dishevelled and tearful, who immediately begins to fight with* FIRE.)

TYLTYL

And who is that wet lady? . . .

THE FAIRY

Don't be afraid, it's Water just come from the tap. . . .

(The milk-jug upsets, falls from the table and smashes on

*the floor; and from the
spilt milk there rises a tall,
white, bashful figure who
seems to be afraid of everything.*)

TYLTYL

And the frightened lady in her night-
gown? . . .

THE FAIRY

That's Milk; she has broken her jug. . . .
(*The sugar-loaf, at the foot
of the cupboard, grows
taller and wider and splits
its paper wrapper, whence
issues a mawkish and hypo-
critical being, dressed in a
long coat half blue and half
white, who goes up to*
MYTYL *with a sanctimoni-
ous smile.*)

MYTYL (*greatly alarmed*)

What does he want? . . .

THE FAIRY

Why, he is the soul of Sugar! . . .

The Blue Bird

MYTYL (*reassured*)

Has he any barley-sugar? . . .

THE FAIRY

His pockets are full of it and each of his
fingers is a sugar-stick. . . .

> (*The lamp falls from the table
> and, at the same moment, its
> flame springs up again and
> turns into a luminous maid
> of incomparable beauty.
> She is dressed in long trans-
> parent and dazzling veils
> and stands motionless in a
> sort of ecstasy.*)

TYLTYL

It's the Queen! . . .

MYTYL

It's the Blessed Virgin! . . .

THE FAIRY

No, my children; it's Light. . . .

> (*Meanwhile, the saucepans on
> the shelves spin round
> like tops; the linen-press
> throws open its folding-
> doors and unrolls a magnifi-*

42

> *cent display of moon-col-*
> *oured and sun-coloured*
> *stuffs, with which mingles*
> *a no less splendid array of*
> *rags and tatters that come*
> *down the ladder from the*
> *loft. But, suddenly, three*
> *loud knocks are heard on*
> *the door at the right.*)

TYLTYL (*alarmed*)

That's daddy! . . . He's heard us! . . .

THE FAIRY

Turn the diamond! . . . From left to
right! . . .

> (TYLTYL *turns the diamond*
> *quickly.*)

Not so quick! . . . Heavens! It's too
late! . . . You turned it too briskly;
they will not have time to resume their
places and we shall have a lot of an-
noyance. . . .

> (*The* FAIRY *becomes an old*
> *woman again, the walls of*
> *the cottage lose their splen-*
> *dour. The Hours go back*

43

into the clock, the spinning-wheel stops, etc. But, in the general hurry and confusion, while FIRE *runs madly round the room, looking for the chimney, one of the loaves of bread, who has been unable to squeeze into the pan, bursts into sobs and utters roars of fright.*)

THE FAIRY

What's the matter? . . .

BREAD (*in tears*)

There's no room in the pan! . . .

THE FAIRY (*stooping over the pan*)

Yes, there is; yes, there is. . . . (*Pushing the other loaves, which have resumed their original places.*) Come, quick, make room there. . . .

(*The knocking at the door is renewed.*)

BREAD (*utterly scared, vainly struggling to enter the pan*)

I can't get in! . . . He'll eat me first! . . .

44

The Blue Bird

THE DOG (*frisking round* TYLTYL)

My little god! . . . I am still here! . . .
    I can still talk! . . . I can still kiss
    you! . . . Once more! Once more!
    Once more! . . .

THE FAIRY

What, you too? . . . Are you there
    still? . . .

THE DOG

What luck! . . . I was too late to re-
    turn to silence; the trap closed too
    quickly. . . .

THE CAT

So did mine. . . . What is going to hap-
    pen? . . . Is there any danger? . . .

THE FAIRY

Well, I'm bound to tell you the truth: all
    those who accompany the two children
    will die at the end of the journey. . . .

THE CAT (*to the* DOG)

Come, let us get back into the trap. . . .

THE DOG

No, no! . . . I won't! . . . I want to
    go with the little god! . . . I want
    to talk to him all the time! . . .

The Blue Bird

THE CAT

Idiot! . . .

(More knocking at the door)

BREAD (*shedding bitter tears*)

I don't want to die at the end of the
journey! . . . I want to get back at
once into my pan! . . .

FIRE (*who has done nothing but run madly
round the room, hissing with anguish*)

I can't find my chimney! . . .

WATER (*vainly trying to get into the tap*)

I can't get into the tap! . . .

SUGAR (*hovering round his paper wrapper*)

I've burst my packing-paper! . . .

MILK (*lymphatically and bashfully*)

Somebody's broken my little jug! . . .

THE FAIRY

Goodness me, what fools they are! . . .
Fools and cowards too! . . . So
you would rather go on living in your
ugly boxes, in your traps and taps,
than accompany the children in search
of the bird? . . .

ALL (*excepting the* DOG *and* LIGHT)

Yes, yes! Now, at once! . . . My tap!

. . . My pan! . . . My chimney! . . . My trap! . . .

THE FAIRY (*to* LIGHT, *who is dreamily gazing at the wreckage of her lamp*)

And you, Light, what do you say?

LIGHT

I will go with the children. . . .

THE DOG (*yelling with delight*)

I too! . . . I too! . . .

THE FAIRY

That's right. . . . Besides, it's too late to go back; you have no choice now, you must all start with us. . . . But you, Fire, don't come near anybody; you, Dog, don't tease the Cat; and you, Water, hold yourself up and try not to run all over the place. . . .

> (*A violent knocking is again heard at the door on the right.*)

TYLTYL (*listening*)

There's daddy again! . . . He's getting up this time; I can hear him walking. . . .

47

The Blue Bird

THE FAIRY

Let us go out by the window. . . . You
shall all come to my house, where I
will dress the Animals and the Things
properly. . . . (*To* BREAD) You,
Bread, take the cage in which to put
the Blue Bird. . . . It will be in your
charge. . . . Quick, quick, let us waste
no time. . . .

>(*The window suddenly lengthens
downwards, like a door.
They all go out; after which
the window resumes its
primitive shape and closes
quite innocently. The room
has become dark again and
the two cots are steeped in
shadow. The door on the
right opens ajar and in the
aperture appear the heads of*
DADDY *and* MUMMY TYL.)

DADDY TYL

It was nothing. . . . It's the cricket
chirping. . . .

48

The Blue Bird

MUMMY TYL

Can you see them? . . .

DADDY TYL

I can. . . . They are sleeping quite quietly. . . .

MUMMY TYL

I can hear their breathing. . . .

(*The door closes again*)

CURTAIN

49

ACT II

SCENE I.—*At the* FAIRY'S

A magnificent entrance-hall in the palace of the FAIRY BÉRYLUNE. *Columns of gleaming marble with gold and silver capitals, staircases, porticoes, balustrades, etc.*

Enter from the back, on the right, sumptuously clad, the CAT, SUGAR *and* FIRE. *They come from a room which emits rays of light; it is the* FAIRY'S *wardrobe. The* CAT *has donned the classic costume of Puss-in-boots;* SUGAR, *a silk dress, half white and half pale-blue; and* FIRE *wears a number of many-coloured aigrettes and a long vermilion mantle lined with gold. They cross the whole length of the hall to the front of the stage, where the* CAT *draws them up under a portico on the right.*

51

THE CAT

This way. I know every inch of this palace. It was left to the Fairy Bérylune by Bluebeard . . . Let us make the most of our last minute of liberty, while the children and Light pay their visit to the Fairy's little daughter. . . . I have brought you here in order to discuss the position in which we are placed. . . . Are we all here? . . .

SUGAR

I see the Dog coming out of the Fairy's wardrobe. . . .

FIRE

What on earth has he got on? . . .

THE CAT

He has put on the livery of one of the footmen of Cinderella's coach. . . . It was just the thing for him. . . . He has the soul of a flunkey. . . . But let us hide behind the balustrade. . . . It's strange how I mistrust him. . . . He had better not hear what I have to say to you. . . .

SUGAR

It is too late. . . . He has discovered
us. . . . Look, here is Water also
coming out of the wardrobe. . . .
Goodness me, how fine she is! . . .

> (*The* DOG *and* WATER *join the
> first group.*)

THE DOG (*frisking about*)

There! There! . . . Aren't we fine! . . .
Just look at these laces and this
embroidery! . . . It's real gold and
no mistake! . . .

THE CAT (*to* WATER)

Is that Catskin's "colour-of-time" dress?
. . . I seem to recognise it. . . .

WATER

Yes, it's the one that suited me best. . . .

FIRE (*between his teeth*)

She's not brought her umbrella. . . .

WATER

What's that? . . .

FIRE

Nothing, nothing. . . .

WATER

I thought you might be speaking of a great
red nose I saw the other day. . . .

THE CAT

Come, don't let us quarrel; we have more
important things to do. . . . We are
only waiting for Bread; where is
he? . . .

THE DOG

He was making an endless fuss about
choosing his dress. . . .

FIRE

Worth while, isn't it, for a fellow who
looks a fool and carries an enormous
stomach? . . .

THE DOG

At last, he decided in favour of a Turkish
robe, adorned with gems, a scimitar
and a turban. . . .

THE CAT

There he is! . . . He has put on Bluebeard's finest dress . . .

Enter BREAD, *in the costume described
above. The silk robe is crossed tightly
over his huge stomach. In one hand*

he holds the hilt of a scimitar passed
through his sash and in the other the
cage intended for the Blue Bird.

BREAD (*waddling conceitedly*)

Well? . . . What do you think of this?

THE DOG (*frisking round the* LOAF)

How nice he looks! What a fool he looks!
How nice he looks! How nice he
looks! . . .

THE CAT (*to the* LOAF)

Are the children dressed? . . .

BREAD

Yes, Master Tyltyl has put on Hop-o'-my-
Thumb's blue jacket and red breeches;
and Miss Mytyl has Gretel's frock
and Cinderella's slippers. . . . But
the great thing was the dressing of
Light! . . .

THE CAT

Why? . . .

BREAD

The Fairy thought her so lovely that she
did not want to dress her at all! . . .
Thereupon I protested in the name of
our dignity as essential and eminently

respectable elements; and I ended by declaring that, under those conditions, I should refuse to be seen with her. . . .

FIRE

They ought to have bought her a lamp-shade! . . .

THE CAT

And what answer did the Fairy make? . . .

THE LOAF

She hit me with her stick on my head and stomach. . . .

THE CAT

And then? . . .

BREAD

I allowed myself to be convinced; but, at the last moment, Light decided on the moonbeam dress at the bottom of the chest with Catskin's treasures. . . .

THE CAT

Come, stop chattering, time presses. . . . Our future is at stake. . . . You have heard—the Fairy has just said so—that the end of this journey will, at the same time, mark the end of our lives.

. . . It is our business, therefore, to prolong it as much as possible and by every possible means. . . . But there is another thing: we must think of the fate of our race and the destiny of our children. . . .

BREAD

Hear, hear! . . . The Cat is right! . . .

THE CAT

Listen to me! . . . All of us here present, Animals, Things and Elements, possess a soul which man does not yet know. That is why we retain a remnant of independence; but, if he finds the Blue Bird, he will know all, he will see all and we shall be completely at his mercy. . . . This is what I have just learned from my old friend, Night, who is also the guardian of the mysteries of Life. . . . It is to our interest, therefore, at all costs to prevent the finding of that bird, even if we have to go so far as to endanger the lives of the children themselves. . . .

57

The Blue Bird

THE DOG (*indignantly*)

What's the fellow saying? . . . Just say
that again, will you, to see if I heard
right? . . .

BREAD

Order! Order! . . . It's not your turn
to speak! . . . I'm in the chair at
this meeting. . . .

FIRE

Who made you chairman? . . .

WATER (*to* FIRE)

Hold your tongue! . . . What are you in-
terfering with? . . .

FIRE

I shall interfere where I choose. . . . And
I want none of your remarks. . . .

SUGAR (*conciliatorily*)

Excuse me. . . . Do not let us quarrel.
. . . This is a serious moment. . . .
We must, above all things, decide
what measures to adopt. . . .

BREAD

I quite agree with Sugar and the Cat. . .

The Blue Bird

The Dog

This is ridiculous! . . . . There is Man
and that's all! . . . We have to obey
him and do as he tells us! . . . That
is the one and only fact! . . . I recognise no one but him! . . . Hurrah
for Man! . . . Man for ever! . . .
In life or death, all for Man! . . .
Man is God! . . .

Bread

I quite agree with the Dog.

The Cat (*to the* Dog)

But at least give your reasons. . . .

The Dog

There are no reasons! . . . I love Man
and that's enough! . . . If you do
anything against him, I will throttle
you first and I will go and tell him
everything. . . .

Sugar (*intervening sweetly*)

Excuse me. . . . Let us not embitter the
discussion. . . . From a certain point
of view, you are both of you right.
. . . There is something to be said on
both sides. . . .

BREAD

I quite agree with SUGAR! . . .

THE CAT

Are we not, all of us, Water, Fire and
you yourselves, Bread and the Dog,
the victims of a nameless tyranny?
. . . Do you remember the time when,
before the coming of the despot, we
wandered at liberty upon the face of
the earth? . . . Fire and Water were
the sole masters of the world; and see
what they have come to! . . . As for
us puny descendants of the great wild
animals. . . . Look out! . . . Pre-
tend to be doing nothing! . . . I see
the Fairy and Light coming. . . .
Light has taken sides with Man; she is
our worst enemy. . . . Here they
are. . . .

Enter, on the right, the FAIRY, *in the
shape of an old woman, and* LIGHT,
followed by TYLTYL *and* MYTYL.

THE FAIRY

Well? . . . What is it? . . . What are

The Blue Bird

you doing in that corner? . . . You
look like conspirators. . . . It is time
to start. . . . I have decided that
Light shall be your leader. . . . You
will obey her as you would me and I
am giving her my wand. . . . The
children will pay a visit to their late
grandparents this evening. . . . You
will remain behind; that is more discreet. . . . They will spend the evening in the bosom of their dead family.
. . . Meanwhile, you will be getting
ready all that is wanted for to-morrow's journey, which will be a long
one. . . . Come, up, be off and every
one to his post! . . .

THE CAT (*hypocritically*)

That is just what I was saying to them,
madam. . . . I was encouraging them
to do their duty bravely and conscien-
tiously; unfortunately, the Dog, who
kept on interrupting me. . . .

THE DOG

What's that? . . . Just wait a bit! . . ..
(*He is about to leap upon the*
61

CAT, *but* TYLTYL, *fore-seeing his intention, stops him with a threatening gesture.*)

TYLTYL

Down, Tylô! . . . Take care; and, if ever I catch you again . . .

THE DOG

My little god, you don't know, it was he who . . .

TYLTYL (*threatening him*)

Be quiet! . . .

THE FAIRY

Come, that will do. . . . Let Bread hand the cage for this evening to Tyltyl. . . . It is just possible that the Blue Bird may be hidden in the Past, at the grandparents'. . . . In any case, it is a chance which we must not neglect. . . . Well, Bread, the cage? . . .

BREAD (*solemnly*)

One moment, if you please, Mrs. Fairy. . . .
(*Like an orator making a speech*)
I call upon all of you to bear witness

62

that this silver cage, which was entrusted to my care by . . .

THE FAIRY (*interrupting him*)

Enough! . . . No speeches! . . . We will
go out this way and the children
that. . . .

TYLTYL (*rather anxiously*)

Are we to go all alone? . . .

MYTYL

I feel hungry! . . .

TYLTYL

I, too! . . .

THE FAIRY (*to* BREAD)

Open your Turkish robe and give them a
slice of your good stomach. . . .

(BREAD *opens his robe, draws
his scimitar and cuts two
slices out of his stomach and
hands them to the* CHIL-
DREN.)

SUGAR (*approaching the* CHILDREN)

Allow me at the same time to offer you a
few sugar-sticks. . . .

(*He breaks off the five fingers of
his left hand, one by one,*

and presents them to the
CHILDREN.)

MYTYL

What is he doing? . . . He is breaking all
his fingers! . . .

SUGAR (*engagingly*)

Taste them, they are capital. . . . They're
made of real barley-sugar. . . .

MYTYL (*tasting one of the fingers*)

Oh, how good they are! . . . Have you
many of them? . . .

SUGAR (*modestly*)

Yes; as many as I want. . . .

MYTYL

Does that hurt you much, when you break
them off? . . .

SUGAR

Not at all. . . . On the contrary, it's a
great advantage; they grow again at
once and so I always have new, clean
fingers. . . .

THE FAIRY

Come, children, don't eat too much sugar.
. . . Don't forget that you are to

have supper presently with your grandpapa and grandmamma. . . .

TYLTYL

Are they here? . . .

THE FAIRY

You shall see them at once. . . .

TYLTYL

How can we see them, when they are
dead? . . .

THE FAIRY

How can they be dead, when they live in
your memory? . . . Men do not
know this secret, because they know
so little; whereas you, thanks to the
diamond, are about to see that the
dead who are remembered live as hap-
pily as though they were not dead. . . .

TYLTYL

Is Light coming with us?

THE FAIRY

No, it is more proper that this visit should
be confined to the family. . . . I will
wait near here, so as not to appear in-
discreet. . . . They did not invite
me. . . .

65

The Blue Bird

TYLTYL

Which way are we to go? . . .

THE FAIRY

Over there. . . . You are on the threshold
of the Land of Memory. . . . As
soon as you have turned the diamond,
you will see a big tree with a board on
it, which will show you that you are
there. . . . But don't forget that you
are to be back, both of you, by a quarter to nine. . . . It is extremely important. . . . Now mind and be punc-
tual, for all would be lost if you were
late. . . . Good-bye for the present!
. . . (*Calling the* CAT, *the* DOG,
LIGHT, *etc.*) This way. . . . And
the little ones that way. . . .

(*She goes out to the right, with*
LIGHT, *the* ANIMALS, *etc.,*
while the CHILDREN *go out*
to the left.)

CURTAIN

The Blue Bird

A thick fog, from which stands out, on the
right, close to the footlights, the trunk
of a large oak, with a board nailed to
it. A vague, milky, impenetrable light
prevails. TYLTYL *and* MYTYL *are at*
the foot of the oak.

TYLTYL

Here is the tree! . . .

MYTYL

There's the board! . . .

TYLTYL

I can't read it. . . . Wait, I will climb up
on this root. . . . That's it. . . . It
says, "Land of Memory."

MYTYL

Is this where it begins? . . .

TYLTYL

Yes, there's an arrow. . . .

MYTYL

Well, where are grandad and granny? . .

TYLTYL

Behind the fog. . . . We shall see. . . .

67

The Blue Bird

MYTYL

I can see nothing at all! . . . I can't see my
feet or my hands. . . . (*Whimper-
ing*) I'm cold! . . . I don't want to
travel any more. . . . I want to go
home. . . .

TYLTYL

Come, don't keep on crying, just like
Water. . . . You ought to be ashamed
of yourself. . . . A great big little
girl like you. . . . Look, the fog is
lifting already. . . . We shall see
what's behind it. . . .

(*The mist begins to move; it
grows thinner and lighter,
disperses, evaporates. Soon,
in a more and more trans-
parent light, appears, under
a leafy vault, a cheerful
little peasant's cottage, covered with creepers. The
door and windows are open.
There are bee-hives under a
shed, flower-pots on the
window-sills, a cage with a*

*sleeping blackbird. Beside
the door is a bench, on
which an old peasant and
his wife, TYLTYL'S grand-
father and grandmother,
are seated, both sound
asleep.*)

TYLTYL (*suddenly recognising them*)

It's grandad and granny! . . .

MYTYL (*clapping her hands*)

Yes! Yes! . . . So it is! So it is! . . .

TYLTYL (*still a little distrustful*)

Take care! . . . We don't know yet if
they can stir. . . . Let's keep behind
the tree. . . .

(GRANNY TYL *opens her eyes,
raises her head, stretches
herself, gives a sigh and
looks at* GAFFER TYL, *who
also wakes slowly from his
sleep.*)

GRANNY TYL

I have a notion that our grandchildren who
are still alive are coming to see us to-
day. . . .

69

GAFFER TYL

They are certainly thinking of us, for I feel anyhow and I have pins and needles in my legs. . . .

GRANNY TYL

I think they must be quite near, for I see tears of joy dancing before my eyes. . . .

GAFFER TYL

No, no, they are a long way off. . . . I still feel weak. . . .

GRANNY TYL

I tell you they are here; I am quite strong. . . .

TYLTYL *and* MYTYL (*rushing up from behind the oak*)

Here we are ! . . . Here we are ! . . . Gaffer ! Granny ! . . . It's we ! . . . It's we ! . . .

GAFFER TYL

There ! . . . You see ? . . . What did I tell you ? . . . I was sure they would come to-day. . . .

GRANNY TYL

Tyltyl ! . . . Mytyl ! . . . It's you ! . . .

70

It's she! . . . (*Trying to run to meet
them*) I can't run! . . . I've still got
the rheumatics! . . .

GAFFER TYL (*hobbling along as fast as he
can*)

No more can I. . . . That's because of my
wooden leg, which I still wear instead
of the one I broke when I fell off the
big oak. . . .

(*The* GRANDPARENTS *and the*
CHILDREN *exchange frantic
embraces.*)

GRANNY TYL

How tall and strong you've grown, Tyltyl!

GAFFER TYL (*stroking* MYTYL'S *hair*)

And Mytyl! . . . Just look at her. . . .
What pretty hair, what pretty
eyes! . . .

GRANNY TYL

Come and kiss me again! . . . Come on to
my lap. . . .

GAFFER TYL

And what about me? . . .

71

GRANNY TYL

No, no. . . . Come to me first. . . . How
    are Daddy and Mummy Tyl? . . .

TYLTYL

Quite well, granny. . . . They were asleep
    when we went out. . . .

GRANNY TYL (*gazing at them and cover-
ing them with caresses*)

Lord, how pretty they are and how nice
    and clean! . . . Was it mummy who
    washed you? . . . And there are no
    holes in your stockings! . . . I used
    to darn them once, you know. . . .
    Why don't you come to see us oftener?
    . . . It makes us so happy! . . . It is
    months and months now that you've
    forgotten us and that we have seen no-
    body. . . .

TYLTYL

We couldn't, granny; and to-day its only
    because of the Fairy. . . .

GRANNY TYL

We are always here, waiting for a visit
    from those who are alive. . . . They
    come so seldom! . . . The last time

you were here, let me see, when was
it? . . . It was on All-hallows, when
the church-bells were ringing. . . .

TYLTYL

All-hallows? . . . We didn't go out that
day, for we both had very bad
colds. . . .

GRANNY TYL

No; but you thought of us. . . .

TYLTYL

Yes. . . .

GRANNY TYL

Well, every time you think of us, we wake
up and see you again. . . .

TYLTYL

What, is it enough to . . .

GRANNY TYL

But come, you know that. . . .

TYLTYL

No, I didn't know. . . .

GRANNY TYL (*to* GAFFER TYL)

It's astonishing, up there. . . . They don't
know yet. . . . Do they never learn
anything? . . .

73

GAFFER TYL

It's as in our own time. . . . The Living are so stupid when they speak of the Others. . . .

TYLTYL

Do you sleep all the time? . . .

GAFFER TYL

Yes, we get plenty of sleep, while waiting for a thought of the Living to come and wake us. . . . Ah, it is good to sleep when life is done. . . . But it is pleasant also to wake up from time to time. . . .

TYLTYL

So you are not really dead? . . .

GAFFER TYL

What do you say? . . . What is he saying? . . . Now he's using words we don't understand. . . . Is it a new word, a new invention? . . .

TYLTYL

The word "dead"? . . .

GAFFER TYL

Yes, that was the word. . . . What does it mean? . . .

74

The Blue Bird

TYLTYL

Why, it means that one's no longer
alive. . . .

GAFFER TYL

How silly they are, up there! . . .

TYLTYL

Is it nice here? . . .

GAFFER TYL

Oh, yes; not bad, not bad; and, if one could
just have a smoke. . . .

TYLTYL

Aren't you allowed to smoke? . . .

GAFFER TYL

Yes, it's allowed; but I've broken my
pipe. . . .

GRANNY TYL

Yes, yes, all would be well, if only you
would come and see us oftener. . . .
Do you remember, Tyltyl? . . . The
last time I baked you a lovely apple-
tart. . . . You ate such a lot of it
that you made yourself ill. . . .

TYLTYL

But I haven't eaten any apple-tart since last

year. . . . There were no apples this
year. . . .

GRANNY TYL

Don't talk nonsense. . . . Here, we have
them always. . . .

TYLTYL

That's different. . . .

GRANNY TYL

What? That's different? . . . Why,
nothing's different when we're able to
kiss each other. . . .

TYLTYL (*looking first at his* GRAND-
MOTHER *and then at his* GRANDFATHER)

You haven't changed, grandad, not a bit,
not a bit. . . . And granny hasn't
changed a bit either. . . . But you're
better-looking. . . .

GAFFER TYL

Well, we feel all right. . . . We have
stopped growing older. . . . But you,
how tall you're growing! . . . Yes,
you're shooting up finely. . . . Look,
over there, on the door, is the mark
of the last time. . . . That was on
All-hallows. . . . Now then, stand

76

up straight. . . . (TYLTYL *stands up
against the door*.) Four fingers taller!
. . . That's immense! . . . (MYTYL
also stands up against the door.) And
Mytyl, four and a half! . . . Aha,
ill weeds grow apace! . . . How
they've grown, oh, how they've
grown! . . .

TYLTYL (*looking around him with
delight*)

Nothing is changed, everything is in its old
place! . . . Only everything is prettier! . . . There is the clock with the
big hand which I broke the point
off. . . .

GAFFER TYL

And here is the soup-tureen you chipped a
corner off. . . .

TYLTYL

And here is the hole which I made in the
door, the day I found the gimlet....

GAFFER TYL

Yes, you've done some damage in your
time! . . . And here is the plum-tree

in which you were so fond of climbing, when I wasn't looking. . . . It
still has its fine red plums. . . .

TYLTYL

But they are finer than ever! . . .

MYTYL

And here is the old blackbird! . . . Does
he still sing? . . .

> (*The blackbird wakes and be-
> gins to sing at the top of
> his voice.*)

GRANNY TYL

You see. . . . As soon as one thinks of
him. . . .

TYLTYL (*observing with amazement that
the blackbird is quite blue*)

But he's blue! . . . Why, that's the bird,
the Blue Bird which I am to take back
to the Fairy. . . . And you never told
us that you had him here! . . . Oh,
he's blue, blue, blue as a blue glass
marble! . . . (*Entreatingly*) Grandad, granny, will you give him to
me? . . .

78

The Blue Bird

GAFFER TYL

Yes, perhaps, perhaps. . . . What do you
think, granny? . . .

GRANNY TYL

Certainly, certainly. . . . What use is he
to us? . . . He does nothing but
sleep. . . . We never hear him
sing. . . .

TYLTYL

I will put him in my cage. . . . I say,
where is my cage? . . . Oh, I know,
I left it behind the big tree. . . . (*He
runs to the tree, fetches the cage and
puts the blackbird into it.*) So, really,
you've really given him to me? . . .
How pleased the Fairy will be! . . .
And Light too! . . .

GAFFER TYL

Mind you, I won't answer for the bird.
. . . I'm afraid that he will never get
used again to the restless life up there
and that he'll come back here by the
first wind that blows this way. . . .
However, we shall see. . . . Leave

79

him there, for the present, and come
and look at the cow. . . .

TYLTYL (*noticing the hives*)

And how are the bees getting on?

GAFFER TYL

Oh, pretty well. . . . They are no longer
alive, as you call it up there; but they
work hard. . . .

TYLTYL (*going up to the hives*)

Oh, yes! . . . I can smell the honey! . . .
How heavy the hives must be! . . .
All the flowers are so beautiful! . . .
And my little dead sisters, are they
here too? . . .

MYTYL

And where are my three little brothers who
were buried? . . .

(*At these words, seven little
CHILDREN, of different
sizes, like a set of Pan's
pipes, come out of the cottage, one by one.*)

GRANNY TYL

Here they are, here they are! . . . As soon
as you think of them, as soon as you

speak of them, they are there, the darlings! . . .

> (TYLTYL *and* MYTYL *run to meet the* CHILDREN. *They hustle and hug one another and dance and whirl about and utter screams of joy.*)

TYLTYL

Hullo, Pierrot! . . . (*They clutch each other by the hair.*) Ah, so we're going to fight again, as in the old days. . . . And Robert! . . . I say, Jean, what's become of your top? . . . Madeleine and Pierette and Pauline! . . . And here's Riquette! . . .

MYTYL

Oh, Riquette, Riquette! . . . She's still crawling on all fours! . . .

GRANNY TYL

Yes, she has stopped growing.

TYLTYL (*noticing the little* DOG *yelping around them*)

There's Kiki, whose tail I cut off with

81

Pauline's scissors. . . . He hasn't
changed either. . . .

GAFFER TYL (*sententiously*)

No, nothing changes here. . . .

TYLTYL

And Pauline still has a pimple on her
nose. . . .

GRANNY TYL

Yes, it won't go away; there's nothing to
be done for it. . . .

TYLTYL

Oh, how well they look, how fat and glossy
they are! . . . What jolly cheeks
they have! . . . They look well
fed. . . .

GRANNY TYL

They have been much better since they
ceased living. . . . There's nothing
more to fear, nobody is ever ill, one
has no anxiety. . . .

(*The clock inside the cottage
strikes eight.*)

GRANNY TYL (*amazed*)

What's that? . . .

82

GAFFER TYL

I don't know, I'm sure. . . . It must be the clock. . . .

GRANNY TYL

It can't be. . . . It never strikes. . . .

GAFFER TYL

Because we no longer think of the time. . . . Was any one thinking of the time? . . .

TYLTYL

Yes, I was. . . . What is the time? . . .

GAFFER TYL

I'm sure I can't tell. . . . I've forgotten how. . . . It struck eight times, so I suppose it's what they call eight o'clock up there. . . .

TYLTYL

Light expects me at a quarter to nine. . . . It's because of the Fairy. . . . It's extremely important. . . . I'm off! . . .

GRANNY TYL

Don't leave us like that, just as supper's ready! . . . Quick, quick, let's lay the table outside. . . . I've got some

capital cabbage-soup and a beautiful
plum-tart. . . .

> (*They get out the table, dishes,
> plates, etc., and lay for sup-
> per outside the door, all
> helping.*)

TYLTYL

Well, as I've got the Blue Bird. . . . And
then it's so long since I tasted cabbage-soup. . . . Ever since I've been
travelling. . . . They don't have it at
the hotels. . . .

GRANNY TYL

There! . . . That didn't take long! . . .
Sit down, children. . . . Don't let us
lose time, if you're in a hurry. . . .

> (*They have lit the lamp and
> served the soup. The*
> GRANDPARENTS *and the*
> CHILDREN *sit down round
> the table, jostling and
> elbowing one another and
> laughing and screaming
> with pleasure.*)

84

The Blue Bird

TYLTYL (*eating like a glutton*)

How good it is! . . . Oh, how good it
is! . . . I want some more! More!
. . . (*He brandishes his wooden
spoon and noisily hits his plate with
it.*)

GAFFER TYL

Come, come, a little more quiet. . . .
You're just as ill-behaved as ever; and
you'll break your plate. . . .

TYLTYL (*half-raising himself on his
stool*)

I want more, more! . . . (*He seizes the
tureen, drags it toward him and upsets it and the soup, which trickles over
the table and down over their knees
and scalds them. Yells and screams
of pain.*)

GRANNY TYL

There! . . . I told you so! . . .

GAFFER TYL (*giving* TYLTYL *a loud box
on the ear*)

That's one for you! . . .

TYLTYL (*staggered for a moment, next*

puts his hand to his cheek with an expres-
sion of rapture)

Oh, that's just like the slaps you used to
give me when you were alive! . . .
Grandad, how nice it was and how
good it makes one feel! . . . I must
give you a kiss! . . .

GAFFER TYL

Very well; there's more where that came
from, if you like them. . . .

(*The clock strikes half-past
eight*)

TYLTYL (*starting up*)

Half-past eight! . . . (*He flings down his
spoon.*)   Myltyl, we've only just got
time! . . .

GRANNY TYL

Oh, I say! . . . Just a few minutes more!
. . . Your house isn't on fire! . . .
We see you so seldom. . . .

TYLTYL

No, we can't possibly. . . . Light is so
kind. . . . And I promised her. . . .
Come, Mytyl, come! . . .

The Blue Bird

GAFFER TYL

Goodness gracious, how tiresome the Living are with all their business and excitement! . . .

TYLTYL (*taking his cage and hurriedly kissing everybody all round*)

Good-bye, grandad. . . . Good-bye, granny. . . . Good-bye, brothers and sisters, Pierrot, Robert, Pauline, Madeleine, Riquette and you, too, Kiki. . . . I feel we mustn't stay. . . . Don't cry, granny; we will come back often. . . .

GRANNY TYL

Come back every day! . . .

TYLTYL

Yes, yes; we will come back as often as we can. . . .

GRANNY TYL

It's our only pleasure and it's such a treat for us when your thoughts visit us! . . .

GAFFER TYL

We have no other amusements. . . .

The Blue Bird

TYLTYL

Quick, quick! . . . My cage! . . . My
bird! . . .

GAFFER TYL (*handing him the cage*)

Here they are! . . . You know, I don't
warrant him; and if he's not the right
colour . . .

TYLTYL

Good-bye! Good-bye! . . .

THE BROTHERS AND SISTERS TYL

Good-bye, Tyltyl! . . . Good-bye,
Mytyl! . . . Remember the barley-
sugar! . . . Good-bye! . . . Come
again! . . . Come again! . . .

> (*They all wave their handker-*
> *chiefs while* TYLTYL *and*
> MYTYL *slowly move away.*
> *But already, during the last*
> *sentences, the fog of the be-*
> *ginning of the scene has*
> *been gradually re-forming,*
> *so that, at the end, all has*
> *disappeared in the mist and,*
> *at the fall of the curtain,*
> TYLTYL *and* MYTYL *are*

*again alone visible under
the big oak.*)

TYLTYL

It's this way, Mytyl. . . .

MYTYL

Where is Light? . . .

TYLTYL

I don't know. . . . (*Looking at the bird in
the cage.*)   But the bird is no longer
blue! . . . He has turned black! . . .

MYTYL

Give me your hand, little brother. . . .
I feel so frightened and so cold. . . .

CURTAIN

ACT III.

SCENE 1.—*The Palace of* NIGHT.

A large and wonderful hall of an austere, rigid, metallic and sepulchral magnificence, giving the impression of a Greek temple with columns, architraves, flagstones and ornaments of black marble, gold and ebony. The hall is trapezium-shaped. Basalt steps, occupying almost the entire width, divide it into three successive stages, which rise gradually toward the back. On the right and left, between the columns, are doors of sombre bronze. At the back, a monumental door of brass. The palace is lit only by a vague light that seems to emanate mainly from the brilliancy of the marble and the ebony. At the rise of the curtain, NIGHT, *in the form of a very old woman, clad in long, black garments, is seated on the steps of the second stage, between two children, of whom one, almost naked, like Cupid, is smiling in a deep sleep, while the other is standing up, motionless and veiled from head to foot.*

Enter from the right, in the foreground, the CAT

NIGHT

Who goes there?

THE CAT (*sinking heavily upon the marble steps*)

It is I, Mother Night. . . . I am worn out. . . .

NIGHT

What's the matter, child? . . . You look pale and thin and you are splashed with mud to your very whiskers. . . . Have you been fighting on the tiles again, in the snow and rain? . . .

THE CAT

It has nothing to do with the tiles! . . .
It's our secret that's at stake! . . .
It's the beginning of the end! . . .

I have managed to escape for a moment to warn you; but I greatly fear that there is nothing to be done. . . .

NIGHT

Why? . . . What has happened? . . .

THE CAT

I have told you of little Tyltyl, the woodcutter's son, and of the magic diamond. . . . Well, he is coming here to demand the Blue Bird of you. . . .

NIGHT

He hasn't got it yet. . . .

THE CAT

He will have it soon, unless we perform some miracle. . . . This is how the matter stands: Light, who is guiding him and betraying us all, for she has placed herself entirely on Man's side, Light has learned that the Blue Bird, the real one, the only one that can live in the light of day, is hidden here, among the blue birds of the dreams that live on the rays of the moon and die as soon as they set eyes on the sun.

93

. . . She knows that she is forbidden
to cross the threshold of your palace,
but she is sending the children; and,
as you cannot prevent Man from opening the doors of your secrets, I do not
know how all this will end. . . . In
any case, if, unfortunately, they should
lay their hands on the real Blue Bird,
there would be nothing for us but to
disappear. . . .

NIGHT

Oh dear, oh dear! . . . What times we
live in! . . . I never have a moment's
peace. . . . I cannot understand Man,
these last few years. . . . What is
he aiming at? . . . Must he absolutely know everything? . . . Already he has captured a third of my
Mysteries, all my Terrors are afraid
and dare not leave the house, my
Ghosts have taken flight, the greater
part of my Sicknesses are ill. . . .

THE CAT

I know, Mother Night, I know, the times
are hard and we are almost alone in

our struggle against Man. . . . But I
hear them coming. . . . I see only one
way: as they are children, we must
give them such a fright that they will
not dare to persist or to open the great
door at the back, behind which they
would find the Birds of the Moon.
. . . The secrets of the other caverns
will be enough to distract their attention and terrify them. . . .

NIGHT (*listening to a sound outside*)

What do I hear? . . . Are there many of
them? . . .

THE CAT

It is nothing; it is our friends, Bread and
Sugar; Water is not very well and
Fire could not come, because he is re-
lated to Light. . . . The Dog is the
only one who is not on our side; but
it is never possible to keep him
away. . . .

(*Enter timidly, on the right, in the foreground*, TYLTYL, MYTYL, BREAD,
SUGAR *and the* DOG.)

95

The Blue Bird

THE CAT (*rushing up to* TYLTYL)

This way, little master, this way. . . . I
have told Night, who is delighted to
see you. . . . You must forgive her,
she is a little indisposed; that is why
she was not able to come to meet
you. . . .

TYLTYL

Good-day, Mrs. Night. . . .

NIGHT (*in an offended voice*)

Good-day? . . . I am not used to that.
. . . You might say, Good-night, or,
at least, Good-evening. . . .

TYLTYL (*mortified*)

I beg your pardon, ma'am. . . . I did not
know. . . . (*Pointing to the two*
CHILDREN.) Are those your two little boys? . . . They are very nice. . . .

NIGHT

This is Sleep. . . .

TYLTYL

Why is he so fat? . . .

NIGHT

That is because he sleeps well. . . .

96

The Blue Bird

TYLTYL

And the other, hiding himself? . . . Why
does he veil his face? . . . Is he ill?
. . . What is his name? . . .

NIGHT

That is Sleep's sister. . . . It is better not
to mention her name. . . .

TYLTYL

Why? . . .

NIGHT

Because her name is not pleasant to hear.
. . . But let us talk of something else.
. . . The Cat tells me that you have
come here to look for the Blue
Bird. . . .

TYLTYL

Yes, ma'am, if you will allow me. . . .
Will you tell me where he is? . . .

NIGHT

I don't know, dear. . . . All I can say
is that he is not here. . . . I have
never seen him. . . .

TYLTYL

Yes, yes. . . . Light told me that he was
here; and Light knows what she is say-

ing. . . . Will you hand me your keys? . . .

NIGHT

But you must understand, dear, that I cannot give my keys like that to the first comer. . . . I have the keeping of all Nature's secrets and I am absolutely forbidden to deliver them to anybody, especially to a child. . . .

TYLTYL

You have no right to refuse them to Man when he asks you for them. . . . I know that. . . .

NIGHT

Who told you? . . .

TYLTYL

Light. . . .

NIGHT

Light again! Always Light! . . . How dare she interfere, how dare she? . . .

THE DOG

Shall I take them from her by force, my little god? . . .

TYLTYL

Hold your tongue, keep quiet and try to be-

98

have. . . . (*To* NIGHT) Come,
madam, give me your keys, please. . . .

NIGHT

Have you the sign, at least? . . . Where is
it? . . .

TYLTYL (*touching his hat*)

Behold the Diamond! . . .

NIGHT (*resigning herself to the inevitable*)

Well, then . . . Here is the key that opens
all the doors of the hall. . . . Look to
yourself if you meet with a misfortune.
. . . I will not be responsible. . . .

BREAD (*very anxiously*)

Is it dangerous? . . .

NIGHT

Dangerous? . . . I will go so far as to say
that I myself do not know what I
shall do when certain of those bronze
doors open upon the abyss. . . . All
around the hall, in each of those basalt
caves, are all the evils, all the
plagues, all the sicknesses, all the terrors, all the catastrophes, all the mysteries that have afflicted life since the
beginning of the world. . . . I have

99

had trouble enough to imprison them there with the aid of Destiny; and it is not without difficulty, I assure you, that I keep some little order among those undisciplined characters. . . . You have seen what happens when one of them escapes and shows itself on earth. . . .

BREAD

My great age, my experience and my devotion make me the natural protector of these two children; therefore, Mrs. Night, permit me to ask you a question. . . .

NIGHT

Certainly. . . .

BREAD

In case of danger, which is the way of escape? . . .

NIGHT

There is no way of escape.

TYLTYL (*taking the key and climbing the first steps*)

Let us begin here. . . . What is behind this bronze door? . . .

The Blue Bird

NIGHT

I think it is the Ghosts. . . . It is long since
    I opened the door and since they came
    out. . . .

TYLTYL (*placing the key in the lock*)

I will see. . . . (*To* BREAD) Have you
    the cage for the Blue Bird? . . .

BREAD (*with chattering teeth*)

I'm not frightened, but don't you think it
    would be better not to open the door,
    but to peep through the keyhole? . . .

TYLTYL

I don't want your advice. . . .

MYTYL (*suddenly beginning to cry*)

I am frightened! . . . Where is Sugar?
    . . . I want to go home! . . .

SUGAR (*eagerly, obsequiously*)

Here I am, miss, here I am. . . . Don't
    cry, I will break off one of my fingers
    so that you may have a sugar-stick. . . .

TYLTYL

Enough of this! . . .

        (*He turns the key and cautiously
        opens the door. Forthwith,
        five or six* GHOSTS *of*

strange and different forms escape and disperse on every side. MYTYL *gives a scream of affright.* BREAD, *terrified, throws away the cage and goes and hides at the back of the hall, while* NIGHT, *running after the* GHOSTS, *cries out to* TYLTYL.)

NIGHT

Quick! Quick! . . . Shut the door! . . . They will all escape and we should never be able to catch them again! . . . They have felt bored in there, ever since Man ceased to take them seriously. . . . (*She runs after the* GHOSTS *and endeavours, with the aid of a whip formed of snakes, to drive them back to the door of their prison.*) Help me! . . . Here! . . . Here! . . .

TYLTYL (*to the* DOG)

Help her, Tylô, at them! . . .

THE DOG (*leaping up and barking*)

Yes, yes, yes! . . .

TYLTYL

And Bread, where's Bread? . . .

BREAD (*at the back of the hall*)

Here. . . . I am near the door to prevent them from going out. . . .

>(*One of the* GHOSTS *moves in that direction and he rushes away at full speed, uttering yells of terror.*)

NIGHT (*to three* GHOSTS *whom she has seized by the neck*)

This way, you! . . . (*To* TYLTYL) Open the door a little. . . . (*She pushes the* GHOSTS *into the cave.*) There, that's it. . . . (*The* DOG *brings up two more.*) And these two. . . . Come, quick, in with you! . . . You know you're only allowed out on All-hallows. . . . (*She closes the door.*)

TYLTYL (*going to another door*)

What's behind this one? . . .

NIGHT

What is the good? . . . I have already told

you the Blue Bird has never been here.
… However, as you please. …
Open the door, if you like. … It's
the Sicknesses. …

TYLTYL (*with the key in the lock.*)
Must I be careful in opening? …

NIGHT

No, it is not worth while. … They
are very quiet, the poor little things.
… They are not happy. … Man,
for some time, has been waging such
a determined war upon them! …
Especially since the discovery of the
microbes. … Open, you will
see. …

(TYLTYL *opens the door quite
wide. Nothing appears.*)

TYLTYL

Don't they come out?

NIGHT

I told you they are almost all poorly and
very much discouraged. … The
doctors are so unkind to them. …
Go in for a moment and see for yourself. …

104

The Blue Bird

(TYLTYL *enters the cavern
and comes out again im-
mediately.*)

TYLTYL

The Blue Bird is not there. . . . They look
very ill, those Sicknesses of yours. . . .
They did not even lift their heads.
. . . (*One little Sickness in slippers, a
dressing-gown and a cotton nightcap
escapes from the cavern and begins to
frisk about the hall.*) Look! . . .
There's a little one escaping. . . .
Which one is it? . . .

NIGHT

It's nothing, one of the smallest; it's Cold-
in-the-Head. . . . It is one of those
which are least persecuted and which
enjoy the best health. . . . (*Calling
to* COLD-IN-THE-HEAD) Come here,
dear. . . . It's too soon yet; you must
wait for the winter. . . . (COLD-IN-
THE-HEAD, *sneezing, coughing and
blowing its nose, returns to the cavern
and* TYLTYL *shuts the door.*)

105

TYLTYL (*going to the next door*)
Let us look at this one. . . . What is in
here? . . .

NIGHT
Take care! . . . It is the Wars. . . .
They are more terrible and powerful
than ever. . . . Heaven knows what
would happen if one of them escaped!
. . . Fortunately, they are rather
heavy and slow-moving. . . . But we
must stand ready to push back the
door, all of us together, while you
take a rapid glance into the
cavern. . . .

(TYLTYL, *with a thousand precautions, opens the door
ajar so that there is only a
little gap to which he can
put his eye. He at once
doubles his back against the
door, shouting.*)

TYLTYL
Quick! Quick! . . . Push with all your
might! . . . They have seen me!

. . . They are all coming! . . . They are breaking down the door! . . .

NIGHT

Come, all together! . . . Push hard! . . . Bread, what are you doing? . . . Push, all of you! . . . How strong they are! . . . Ah, that's it! . . . They are giving way! . . . It was high time! . . . Did you see them? . . .

TYLTYL

Yes, yes! . . . They are huge and awful! . . . I don't think that they have the Blue Bird. . . .

NIGHT

You may be sure they haven't. . . . If they had, they would eat him at once. . . . Well, have you had enough of it? . . . You see there is nothing to be done. . . .

TYLTYL

I must see everything. . . . Light said so. . . .

NIGHT

Light said so! . . . It's an easy thing to

say when one's afraid and stays at home. . . .

CENTER: **TYLTYL**

Let us go to the next. . . . What is in here? . . .

CENTER: **NIGHT**

This is where I lock up the Shades and the Terrors. . . .

CENTER: **TYLTYL**

Can I open the door? . . .

CENTER: **NIGHT**

Certainly. . . . They are pretty quiet; they are like the Sicknesses. . . .

TYLTYL (*half-opening the door, with a certain mistrustfulness, and taking a look into the cavern*)

Are they not there? . . .

NIGHT (*looking into the cavern in her turn*)

Well, Shades, what are you doing? . . . Come out for a moment and stretch your legs; it will do you good. . . . And the Terrors also. . . . There is nothing to be afraid of. . . . (*A few* SHADES *and a few* TERRORS, *in the*

CENTER: 108

shape of women, shrouded, the former
in black veils and the latter in green-
ish veils, piteously venture to take a
few steps outside the cavern; and
then, upon a movement of TYLTYL's,
hastily run back again.) Come, don't
be afraid. . . . It's only a child; he
won't hurt you. . . . (To TYLTYL)
They have become extremely timid,
except the great ones, those whom you
see at the back. . . .

TYLTYL (looking into the depths of the
cave)

Oh, how terrifying they are! . . .

NIGHT

They are chained up. . . . They are the
only ones that are not afraid of Man.
. . . But shut the door, lest they
should grow angry. . . .

TYLTYL (going to the next door)

I say! . . . This is a darker one. . . .
What is here?

NIGHT

There are several Mysteries behind this
one. . . . If you are absolutely bent

109

upon it, you may open it too. . . .
But don't go in. . . . Be very cautious
and let us get ready to push back the
door, as we did with the Wars. . . .

TYLTYL (*half-opening the door; with un-
parlleled precautions and passing his
head fearsomely through the aperture*)

Oh! . . . How cold! . . . My eyes are
smarting! . . . Shut it quickly! . . .
Push, oh, push! They are pushing
against us! . . . (NIGHT, *the* DOG,
the CAT *and* SUGAR *push back the
door*.) Oh, I saw! . . .

NIGHT

What? . . .

TYLTYL (*upset*)

I don't know, it was awful! . . . They
were all seated like monsters without eyes. . . . Who was the giant
who tried to seize me? . . .

NIGHT

It was probably Silence; he has charge of
this door. . . . It appears to have

been alarming? . . . You are quite
pale still and trembling all over. . . .

TYLTYL

Yes, I would never have believed. . . . I
had never seen. . . . And my hands
are frozen. . . .

NIGHT

It will be worse presently if you
go on. . . .

TYLTYL (*going to the next door*)

And this one? . . . Is this terrible
also? . . .

NIGHT

No; there is a little of everything here.
. . . It is where I keep the unem-
ployed Stars, my personal Perfumes,
a few Glimmers that belong to me,
such as Will-o'-the-Wisps, Glow-
worms and Fireflies, also the Dew, the
Song of the Nightingales and so
on. . . .

TYLTYL

Just so, the Stars, the Song of the Nightingales. . . . This must be the door. . . .

The Blue Bird

Open it, if you like; there is nothing very bad inside. . . .

> (TYLTYL *throws the door wide open. The* STARS, *in the shape of beautiful young girls veiled in many-coloured radiancy, escape from their prison, disperse over the hall and form graceful groups on the steps and around the columns, bathed in a sort of luminous penumbra. The* PERFUMES OF THE NIGHT, *who are almost invisible, the* WILL-O'-THE-WISPS, *the* FIREFLIES *and the transparent* DEW *join them, while the* SONG OF THE NIGHTINGALES *streams from the cavern and floods the Palace of* NIGHT.)

MYTYL (*clapping her hands with delight*)
Oh, what pretty ladies! . . .

TYLTYL
And how well they dance! . . .

MYTYL
And how sweet they smell! . . .

TYLTYL
And how beautifully they sing! . . .

MYTYL
What are those. whom one can hardly
see? . . .

NIGHT
Those are the Perfumes of my Shadow.

TYLTYL
And those others, over there, in spun
glass? . . .

NIGHT
They are the Dew of the plains and forests.
. . . But enough! . . . They would
never have done. . . . It is the devil's
own business to get them back, once
they begin to dance. . . . (*Clapping
her hands together.*) Now then,
Stars, quick! . . . This is not the time

for dancing. . . . The sky is overcast
and heavily clouded. . . . Come,
quick, in with you, or I will go and
fetch a ray of sunlight! . . . (*The
STARS, PERFUMES, etc., take to flight
in dismay and rush back into the cavern; and the door is closed upon them.
At the same time, the song of the
NIGHTINGALE ceases.*)

TYLTYL (*going to the door at the back*)
Here is the great middle door. . . .

NIGHT (*gravely*)
Do not open that one. . . .

TYLTYL
Why not? . . .

NIGHT
Because it's not allowed. . . .

TYLTYL
Then it's here that the Blue Bird is hidden;
Light told me so. . . .

NIGHT (*maternally*)
Listen to me, child. . . . I have been kind
and indulgent. . . . I have done for
you what I have never done for any
one before. . . . I have given up all

114

my secrets to you. . . . I like you, I feel pity for your youth and innocence and I am speaking to you as a mother. . . . Listen to me, my child, and believe me; relinquish your quest, go no further, do not tempt fate, do not open that door. . . .

TYLTYL (*a little shaken*)

But why? . . .

NIGHT

Because I do not wish you to be lost. . . . Because not one of those, do you hear, not one of those who have opened it, were it but by a hair's breadth, has ever returned alive to the light of day. . . . Because every awful thing imaginable, because all the terrors, all the horrors of which men speak on earth are as nothing compared with the most harmless of those which assail a man from the moment when his eye lights upon the first threats of the abyss to which no one dares give a name. . . . So much so that I myself, if you are bent, in spite of everything,

115

upon touching that door, will ask you to wait until I have sought safety in my windowless tower. . . . Now it is for you to know, for you to reflect. . . .

> (MYTYL, *all in tears, utters cries of inarticulate terror and tries to drag* TYLTYL *away*.)

BREAD (*with chattering teeth*)

Don't do it, master dear! . . . (*Flinging himself on his knees*) Take pity on us! . . . I implore you on my knees. . . . You see that Night is right. . . .

THE CAT

You are sacrificing the lives of all of us. . . .

TYLTYL

I must open the door. . . .

MYTYL (*stamping her feet, amid her sobs*) I won't! . . . I sha'n't! . . .

TYLTYL

Sugar and Bread, take Mytyl by the hand and run away with her. . . . I am going to open the door. . . .

The Blue Bird

NIGHT

Run for your lives! . . . Come quickly! . . . It is time! . . . (*She flees.*)

BREAD (*fleeing wildly*)

At least wait till we are at the end of the hall! . . .

THE CAT (*also fleeing*)

Wait! Wait! . . .

(*They hide behind the columns at the other end of the hall. TYLTYL remains alone with the DOG by the monumental door.*)

THE DOG (*panting and hiccoughing with suppressed fright*)

I shall stay, I shall stay! . . . I'm not afraid! . . . I shall stay! . . . I shall stay with my little god! . . . I shall stay! . . . I shall stay! . . .

TYLTYL (*patting the DOG*)

That's right, Tylô, that's right! . . . Kiss me. . . . You and I are two. . . . And now, steady! . . .

(*He places the key in the lock. A cry of alarm comes from*

117

*the other end of the hall,
where the runaways have
taken refuge. The key has
hardly touched the door
before its tall and wide
leaves open in the mid-
dle, glide apart and disappear on either side in the
thickness of the walls, suddenly revealing the most un-
expected of gardens, un-
real, infinite and ineffable, a
dream-garden bathed in
nocturnal light, where,
among stars and planets, il-
lumining all that they touch,
flying ceaselessly from jewel
to jewel and from moon-
beam to moonbeam, fairy-
like blue birds hover per-
petually and harmoniously
down to the confines of the
horizon, birds innumerable,
to the point of appearing
to be the breath, the azured*

atmosphere, the very sub-
stance of the wonderful gar-
den.)

TYLTYL (*dazzled, bewildered, standing in*
the light of the garden)

Oh! . . . Heaven! . . . (*Turning to those*
who have fled)   Come quickly! . . .
They are here! . . . It's they, it's
they, it's they! . . . We have them at
last! . . . Thousands of blue birds!
. . . Millions! . . . Thousands of
millions! . . . There will be too
many! . . . Come, Mytyl! . . .
Come, Tylô! . . . Come, all! . . .
Help me! . . . (*Darting in among*
the birds.)   You can catch them by
handfuls! . . . They are not shy!
. . . They are not afraid of us! . . .
Here! Here! . . . (MYTYL *and the*
others run up. *They all enter the*
dazzling garden, except NIGHT *and*
the CAT.)   You see! . . . There are
too many of them! . . . They fly
into my hands! . . . Look, they are
eating the moonbeams! . . . Mytyl,

where are you? . . . There are so
many blue wings, so many feathers
falling that one cannot see anything
for them! . . . Don't bite them,
Tylô! . . . Don't hurt them! . . .
Take them very gently! . . .

MYTYL (*covered with blue birds*)

I have caught seven already! . . . Oh,
how they flap their wings! . . . I
can't hold them! . . .

TYLTYL

Nor can I! . . . I have too many of
them! . . . They're escaping! . . .
They're coming back! . . . Tylô has
some, too! . . . They will drag us
with them! . . . They will take us up
to the sky! . . . Quick, let us go
out this way! . . . Light is waiting
for us! . . . How pleased she will
be! . . .

This way, this way! . . .

(*They escape from the garden,
with their hands full of
struggling birds, and, crossing the whole hall amid the*

*mad whirl of the azure
wings, go out on the right,
where they first entered, followed by* BREAD *and* SUGAR,
who have caught no birds.
NIGHT *and the* CAT, *left
alone, return to the back of
the stage and look anxiously
into the garden.*)

NIGHT

Haven't they got him? . . .

THE CAT

No. . . . I see him there, on that moonbeam. . . . They could not reach him,
he kept too high. . . .

(*The* CURTAIN *falls. Immediately after, before the
dropped curtain,* ENTER,
*at the same time, on the
left,* LIGHT *and, on the
right,* TYLTYL, MYTYL *and
the* DOG, *who run up all
covered by the birds which
they have captured. But
already the birds appear*

lifeless and, with hanging heads and drooping wings, are nothing more in their hands than inert remains.)

LIGHT

Well, have you caught him? . . .

TYLTYL

Yes, yes! . . . As many as we wanted! . . . There are thousands of them! . . . Here they are! . . . Do you see them? . . . (*Looking at the birds, which he holds out to* LIGHT, *and perceiving that they are dead*) Why, they are dead! . . . What have they done to them? . . . Yours, too, Mytyl? . . . Tylô's also? . . . (*Angrily flinging down the dead bodies of the birds*) Oh, this is too bad? . . . Who killed them? . . . I am too unhappy! . . . (*He hides his head in his arms and his whole frame is shaken with sobs.*)

LIGHT (*pressing him maternally in her arms*)

Do not cry, my child. . . . You did not
catch the one that is able to live in
broad daylight. . . . He has gone
elsewhere. . . . We shall find him
again. . . .

THE DOG (*looking at the dead birds*)
Are they good to eat? . . .

(*They all go out on the left.*)

SCENE 2.—*The Forest*

*A forest. It is night. The moon is shin-
ing. Old trees of various kinds, notably an* OAK, *a* BEECH, *an* ELM, *a*
POPLAR, *a* FIR-TREE, *a* CYPRESS, *a*
LIME-TREE, *a* CHESTNUT-TREE, *etc.*

ENTER *the* CAT.

THE CAT (*bowing to the trees in turn*)
To all the trees here present, greeting! . . .
THE TREES (*murmuring in their leaves*)
Greeting! . . .

THE CAT
This is a great day, a day of days! . . .
Our enemy is coming to set free your

123

energies and to deliver himself into
your hands. . . . It is Tyltyl, the son
of the wood-cutter, who has done you
so much harm. . . . He is seeking
the Blue Bird, whom you have kept
hidden from Man since the beginning
of the world and who alone knows
our secret. . . . (*A murmuring in the
leaves.*) What do you say? . . . Ah,
it's the Poplar! . . . Yes, he pos-
sesses a diamond which has the
virtue of setting free our spirits for
a moment; he can compel us to hand
over the Blue Bird and thenceforth
we shall be definitely at Man's mercy.
. . . (*A murmuring in the leaves.*)
Who is speaking? . . . Ah, the
Oak! . . . How are you? . . . (*A
murmuring in the leaves of the* OAK.)
Still got your cold? . . . Does the
Liquorice no longer look after you?
. . . Can't you throw off your rheu-
matism? . . . Believe me, that's because of the moss; you put too much
of it on your feet. . . . Is the Blue

The Blue Bird

Bird still with you? . . . (*A murmuring in the leaves of the* OAK.) I beg your pardon? . . . Yes, there is no room for hesitation; we must take the opportunity; he must he done away with. . . . (*A murmuring in the leaves.*) I didn't quite catch. . . . Oh, yes, he is with his little sister; she must die, too. . . . (*A murmuring in the leaves.*) Yes, they have the Dog with them; there is no keeping him away. . . . (*A murmuring in the leaves.*) What did you say? . . . Bribe him? . . . Impossible. . . . I have tried everything. . . . (*A murmuring in the leaves.*) Ah, is that you, Fir-Tree? . . . Yes, get four planks ready. . . . Yes, there are Fire, Sugar, Water and Bread besides. . . . They are all with us, except Bread, who is rather doubtful. . . . Light alone is on Man's side; but she won't come. . . . I made the children believe that they ought to steal away while she was asleep. . . . There

never was such an opportunity. . . .
(*A murmuring in the leaves.*) Ah,
that's the Beech's voice! . . . Yes,
you are right; we must inform the
animals. . . . Has the Rabbit got his
drum? . . . Is he with you? . . .
Good, let him beat the troop at
once. . . . Here they are! . . .

> (*The roll of the* RABBIT'S *drum
> is heard, diminishing in the
> distance. Enter* TYLTYL,
> MYTYL *and the* DOG.)

TYLTYL

Is this the place? . . .

THE CAT (*obsequiously, eagerly, mealy-
mouthed, rushing to meet the* CHIL-
DREN)

Ah, there you are, my little master! . . .
How well you look and how pretty,
this evening! . . . I went before you
to announce your arrival. . . . All is
going well. We shall have the Blue
Bird to-night, I am sure. . . . I have
just sent the Rabbit to beat the troop
in order to convoke the principal ani-

126

mals of the country. . . . You can hear them already among the foliage. . . . Listen! . . . They are a little shy and dare not come near. . . . (*The sounds are heard of different animals, such as cows, pigs, horses, donkeys, etc. The* CAT, *aside, to* TYLTYL, *taking him apart*) But why have you brought the Dog? . . . I have told you he is on the worst terms with everybody, even the trees. . . . I fear that his odious presence will spoil everything. . . .

TYLTYL

I could not get rid of him. . . . (*To the* DOG, *threatening him*) Go away, you ugly thing! . . .

THE DOG

Who? . . . I? . . . Why? . . . What have I done? . . .

TYLTYL

I tell you, go away! . . . We don't want you here and there's an end of it. . . . You're a nuisance, there! . . .

127

THE DOG

I sha'n't say a word. . . . I shall follow you at a distance. . . . They sha'n't see me. . . . Shall I beg? . . .

THE CAT (*aside, to* TYLTYL)

Do you allow this disobedience? . . . Hit him on the nose with your stick; he is really unbearable! . . .

TYLTYL (*beating the* DOG)

There, that will teach you to be more obedient! . . .

THE DOG (*yelling*)

Ow! Ow! Ow! . . .

TYLTYL

What do you say? . . .

THE DOG

I must kiss you now you've beaten me! . . . (*He covers* TYLTYL *with violent kisses and embraces.*)

TYLTYL

Come. . . . That will do. . . . That's enough. . . . Go away! . . .

MYTYL

No, no; I want him to stay. . . . I am

128

afraid of everything when he is not there. . . .

THE DOG (*leaping up and almost upsetting* MYTYL, *whom he overwhelms with hurried and enthusiastic kisses*)

Oh, the dear little girl! . . . How beauti- ful she is! . . . How good she is! . . . How beautiful she is, how sweet she is! . . . I must kiss her! . . . Once more, once more, once more! . . .

THE CAT

What an idiot! . . . Well, we shall see! . . . Let us lose no time. . . . Turn the diamond. . . .

TYLTYL

Where shall I stand? . . .

THE CAT

In this moonbeam; you will see better. . . . There, turn it gently! . . .

(TYLTYL *turns the Diamond. A long-drawn-out rustling shakes the leaves and branches. The oldest and most stately trunks open to make way for the soul which*

129

*each of them contains. The
appearance of these souls
differs according to the appearance and the character
of the trees which they re-
present. The soul of the
ELM, for instance, is a sort
of pursy, pot-bellied, crabbed
gnome; the LIME-TREE is
placid, familiar and jovial;
the BEECH, elegant and
agile; the BIRCH, white, re-
served and restless; the
WILLOW, stunted, dishev-
elled and plaintive; the FIR-
TREE, tall, lean and taciturn;
the CYPRESS, tragic; the
CHESTNUT-TREE, preten-
tious and rather dandified;
the POPLAR, sprightly, cum-
bersome, talkative. Some
emerge slowly from their
trunks, torpidly stretching
themselves, as though they
had been imprisoned or*

asleep for ages; others leap out actively, eagerly; and all come and stand in a circle round the two CHILDREN, *while keeping as near as they can to the tree in which they were born.*)

THE POPLAR (*running up first and screaming at the top of his voice*)

Men? . . . Little men! . . . We shall be able to talk to them! . . . We've done with silence! . . . Done with it! . . . Where do they come from? . . . Who are they? . . . What are they? . . . (*To the* LIME-TREE, *who comes forward quietly smoking his pipe*) Do you know them, Daddy Lime-Tree? . . .

THE LIME-TREE

I do not remember ever having seen them. . . .

THE POPLAR

Oh, yes, you must have! . . . You know all the men; you're always hanging about their houses. . . .

THE LIME-TREE (*examining the*
CHILDREN)

No, I assure you. . . . I don't know
them. . . . They are too young still.
. . . I only know the lovers who come
to see me by moonlight and the topers
who drink their beer under my
branches. . . .

THE CHESTNUT-TREE (*affectedly adjust-
ing his eyeglass*)

Who are these? . . . Are they poor people
from the country? . . .

THE POPLAR

Oh, as for you, Mr. Chestnut-Tree, ever
since you have refused to show yourself except in the streets of the big
towns . . .

THE WILLOW (*hobbling along in a pair of
wooden shoes*)

Oh dear, oh dear! . . . They have come
to cut off my head and arms again
for fagots! . . .

THE POPLAR

Silence! . . . Here is the Oak leaving his
palace! . . . He looks far from well

132

this evening. . . . Don't you think he is growing very old? . . . What can his age be? . . . The Fir-tree says he is four thousand; but I am sure that he exaggerates. . . . Listen; he will tell us all about it. . . .

> (*The* OAK *comes slowly forward. He is fabulously old, crowned with mistletoe and clad in a long green gown edged with moss and lichen. He is blind; his white beard streams in the wind. He leans with one hand on a knotty stick and with the other on a young* OAKLING, *who serves as his guide. The Blue Bird is perched on his shoulder. At his approach, the other trees draw themselves up in a row and bow respectfully.*)

TYLTYL

He has the Blue Bird! . . . Quick!

133

Quick! . . . Here! . . . Give it to
me! . . .

The Trees

Silence! . . .

The Cat (*to* Tyltyl)

Take off your hat, it's the Oak! . . .

The Oak (*to* Tyltyl)

Who are you? . . .

Tyltyl

I am Tyltyl, sir. . . . When can I have the
Blue Bird? . . .

The Oak

Tyltyl, the wood-cutter's son? . . .

Tyltyl

Yes, sir. . . .

The Oak

Your father has done us much harm. . . .
In my family alone, he has put to
death six hundred of my sons, four
hundred and seventy-five uncles and
aunts, twelve hundred cousins of both
sexes, three hundred and eighty daugh-
ters-in-law, and twelve thousand great-
grandsons! . . .

moss slippers! . . . It will be such a
joke! . . .

TYLTYL

Hold your tongue! . . . And be off with
you! . . . Be off, you ugly brute! . . .

THE DOG

All right, all right, I'm going. . . . I'll
come back when you want me. . . .

THE CAT (*aside, to* TYLTYL)

It would be a good thing to chain him up,
or he will commit some folly; the
Trees will be angry and all will end
badly. . . .

TYLTYL

What can I do? . . . I have lost his
leash. . . .

THE CAT

Here's the Ivy just coming along with
strong bonds. . . .

THE DOG (*growling*)

I'll come back, I'll come back! . . . Ugh!
Goutytoes! Timbertoes! . . . Pack
of old stunted growths, pack of old
roots! . . . It's the Cat who's at the
bottom of all this! . . . I'll be even

with him! . . . What have you been
whispering about, you sneak, you
tiger, you Judas! . . . Wow, wow,
wow! . . .

THE CAT
You see, he insults everybody. . . .

TYLTYL
Yes, he is unbearable and one can't hear
one's self speak. . . . Mr. Ivy, will
you chain him up, please? . . .

THE IVY (*timorously going up to the* DOG)
Won't he bite? . . .

THE DOG (*growling*)
On the contrary, on the contrary! . . .
He's going to kiss you! . . . Just
wait and see! . . . Come along, come
along, you old ball of twine, you! . . .

TYLTYL (*threatening him with his stick*)
Tylô! . . .

THE DOG (*cringing at* TYLTYL'S *feet and wagging his tail*)
What am I to do, my little god?

TYLTYL

Lie down flat! . . . Obey the Ivy. . . . .
Let him bind you, or. . . .

THE DOG (*growling between his teeth,
while the* IVY *binds him*)

Ball of twine! . . . Hunk of yarn! . . .
Hangman's rope! . . . Calves' leash!
. . . Look, my little god! . . . He's
cutting my paws! . . . He's choking
me! . . .

TYLTYL

I don't care! . . . It's your own fault. . . .
Hold your tongue; be quiet; you're
unbearable! . . .

THE DOG

You're wrong, for all that. . . . They
mean mischief. . . . Take care, my
little god! . . . He's closing my
mouth! . . . I can't speak! . . .

THE IVY (*who has tied up the* DOG *like a
parcel*)

Where shall we put him? . . . I've muz-
zled him finely. . . . He can't utter a
word. . . .

141

THE OAK

Fasten him tight down there, behind my trunk, to my big root. . . . We will decide later what had best be done with him. . . .

> (*The* IVY *and the* POPLAR *carry the* DOG *behind the* OAK's *trunk.*)

THE OAK

Is that done? . . . Well, now that we are rid of this inconvenient witness, of this renegade, let us deliberate in accordance with justice and truth. . . . I will not conceal from you the deep and painful nature of my emotion. . . . This is the first time that it is given to us to judge Man and make him feel our power. . . . I do not think that, after the harm which he has done us, after the monstrous injustice which we have suffered, there can remain the least doubt as to the sentence that awaits him. . . .

ALL THE TREES *and* ALL THE ANIMALS

No! No! No! . . . No doubt at all! . . .

Hanging! . . . Death! . . . The
injustice has been too great! . . .
The abuse too wicked! . . . It has
lasted too long! . . . Crush him! . . .
Eat him! . . . At once! . . . Here
and now! . . .

TYLTYL (*to the* CAT)

What is the matter with them? . . . Are
they displeased? . . .

THE CAT

Don't be alarmed. . . . They are a little
annoyed because Spring is late. . . .
Leave it to me; I will settle it
all. . . .

THE OAK

This unanimity was inevitable. . . . We
must now decide, in order to avoid
reprisals, which form of execution will
be the most practical, the easiest, the
quickest and the safest, which will
leave the fewest accusing traces when
Man finds the little bodies in the
forest. . . .

TYLTYL

What is all this about? . . . What is he

143

driving at? . . . I am getting tired of this. . . . He has got the Blue Bird; let him hand it over. . . .

THE BULL (*coming forward*)

The most practical and the surest way is a good butt with the horns in the pit of the stomach. . . . Shall I go at him? . . .

THE OAK

Who speaks? . . .

THE CAT

It's the Bull.

THE COW

It would be better to keep quiet. . . . I won't meddle with it. . . . I have all the grass to browse in the field which you can see down there in the blue light of the moon. . . . I have quite enough to do. . . .

THE OX

I also. . . . However, I agree to everything beforehand. . . .

THE BEECH

I can offer my highest branch to hang them on. . . .

144

The Blue Bird

THE IVY

And I the slip-knot. . . .

THE FIR-TREE

And I the four planks for their little coffin. . . .

THE CYPRESS

And I a perpetual grant of a tomb. . . .

THE WILLOW

The simplest way would be to drown them in one of my rivers. . . . I will take charge of that. . . .

THE LIME-TREE (*in a conciliatory tone*)

Come, come. . . . Is it really necessary to go to such extremities? . . . They are very young. . . . We could quite simply prevent them from doing any harm by keeping them prisoners in an enclosure which I will undertake to form by planting myself all around. . . .

THE OAK

Who speaks? . . . I seem to recognise the honeyed accents of the Lime-tree. . . .

THE FIR-TREE

Yes, it's he. . . .

145

THE OAK

So there is a renegade among us, as among
the Animals? . . . Hitherto we have
only had to deplore the disloyalty of
the Fruit-trees; but they are not real
trees. . . .

THE PIG (*rolling his small eyes glutton-ously*)

I think we should first eat the little
girl. . . . She ought to be very tender. . . .

TYLTYL

What's he saying? . . . Just wait a bit,
you . . .

THE CAT

I don't know what is the matter with them;
but things are beginning to look
badly. . . .

THE OAK

Silence! . . . What we have to decide is
which of us shall have the honour of
striking the first blow, who shall ward
off from our tops the greatest danger
that has threatened us since the birth
of Man. . . .

The Blue Bird

The Fir-tree

That honour falls to you, our king and our
    patriarch. . . .

The Oak

Is that the Fir-tree speaking? . . . Alas,
    I am too old! . . . I am blind and in-
    firm and my numbed arms no longer
    obey me. . . . No, to you, brother,
    ever green, ever upright, to you, who
    have witnessed the birth of most of
    these trees, to you be the glory, in de-
    fault of myself, of the noble act of our
    deliverance. . . .

The Fir-tree

I thank you, venerable father. . . . But
    as I shall, in any case, have the honour
    of burying the two victims, I should be
    afraid of arousing the just jealousy of
    my colleagues; and I think that, next
    to ourselves, the oldest and the worthi-
    est and the one that owns the best
    club is the Beech. . . .

The Beech

You know I am worm-eaten and my club is
    no longer to be relied upon. . . . But

the Elm and the Cypress have powerful weapons. . . .

THE ELM

I should be only too pleased; but I can
hardly stand upright. . . . A mole
twisted my great toe last night. . . .

THE CYPRESS

As for me, I am ready. . . . But, like my
brother, the Fir-tree, I shall have, if
not the privilege of burying them, at
least the advantage of weeping over
their tomb. . . . It would be an un-
lawful plurality of offices. . . . Ask
the Poplar. . . .

THE POPLAR

Me? . . . Are you serious? . . . Why,
my wood is more tender than the flesh
of a child! . . . And, besides, I don't
know what's the matter with me. . . .
I am shivering with fever. . . . Just
look at my leaves. . . . I must have
caught cold at sunrise this morning. . . .

THE OAK (*bursting out with indignation*)
You are afraid of Man! . . . Even those

unprotected and unarmed little children inspire you with the mysterious
terror which has always made us the
slaves that we are! . . . Enough of
this! Things being as they are and
the opportunity unequalled, I shall go
forth alone, old, crippled, trembling,
blind as I am, against the hereditary
enemy! . . . Where is he? . . .

> (*Groping with his stick, he
> moves towards* TYLTYL.)

TYLTYL (*taking his knife from his pocket*)
Is it me he's after, that old one, with his
big stick? . . .

ALL THE TREES (*uttering a cry of alarm
at the sight of the knife, they step in
between and hold back the* OAK)
The knife! . . . Take care! . . . The
knife! . . .

> THE OAK (*struggling*)
Let me be! . . . What does it matter? . . .
The knife or the axe! . . . Who's
holding me back? . . . What! Are
you all here? . . . What! You all
want to. . . . (*Flinging down his*

149

stick) Well, so be it! . . . Shame upon us! . . . Let the Animals deliver us! . . .

THE BULL

That's right! . . . I'll see to it! . . . And with one blow of the horns! . . .

THE OX *and* THE COW (*holding him back by the tail*)

What are you doing? . . . Don't be a fool! . . . It's a bad business! . . . It will end badly. . . . It is we who will pay for it. . . . Do let be. . . . It's the wild animals' business. . . .

THE BULL

No, no! . . . It's my business! . . . Wait and see! . . . Look here, hold me back or there will be an accident! . . .

TYLTYL (*to* MYTYL, *who is uttering piercing screams*)

Don't be afraid! . . . Stand behind me. . . . I have my knife. . . .

THE COCK

He has plenty of pluck, the little chap! . . .

150

The Blue Bird

TYLTYL

So you've made up your minds, it's me
    you're going for? . . .

THE ASS

Why, of course, my little man; you've taken
    long enough to see it! . . .

THE PIG

You can say your prayers; your last hour
    has come. . . . But don't hide the
    little girl. . . . I want to feast my
    eyes on her. . . . I'm going to eat her
    first. . . .

TYLTYL

What have I done to you? . . .

THE SHEEP

Nothing at all, my little man. . . . Eaten
    my little brother, my two sisters, my
    three uncles, my aunt, my grandpapa
    and my grandmamma. . . . Wait,
    wait, when you're down, you shall see
    that I have teeth also. . . .

THE ASS

And I hoofs! . . .

THE HORSE (*haughtily pawing the
    ground*)

151

You shall see what you shall see! . . .
Would you rather that I tore you with
my teeth or knocked you down with a
kick? . . . (*He moves ostentatiously
towards* TYLTYL, *who faces him and
raises his knife. Suddenly the* HORSE,
*seized with panic, turns and rushes
away.*) Ah, no! . . . That's not
fair! . . . That's against the rules!
. . . He's defending himself! . . .

THE COCK (*unable to hide his admiration*)
I don't care, the little chap's full of
grit! . . .

THE PIG (*to the* BEAR *and the* WOLF)
Let us all rush on them together. . . . I
will support you from the rear. . . .
We will throw them down and share
the little girl when she is on the
ground. . . .

THE WOLF
Divert their attention in front. . . . I am
going to make a turning movement. . . .
(*He goes round* TYLTYL, *whom
he attacks from behind and
half overthrows.*)

152

TYLTYL

You brute! . . . (*He raises himself on one knee brandishing his knife and doing his best to cover his little sister, who utters yells of distress. Seeing him half overturned, all the* ANIMALS *and* TREES *come up and try to hit him.* TYLTYL *calls distractedly for assistance.*) Help! Help! . . . Tylô! Tylô! . . . Where is the Cat? . . . Tylô! . . . Tylette! Tylette! . . . Come! Come! . . .

THE CAT (*hypocritically, holding aloof*)

I can't come. . . . I have sprained my paw. . . .

TYLTYL (*warding off the blows and defending himself as best he can*)

Help! . . . Tylô! Tylô! . . . I can't hold out! . . . There are too many of them! . . . The Bear! The Pig! The Donkey! The Ass! The Fir-tree! The Beech! . . . Tylô! Tylô! Tylô! . . .

(*Dragging his broken bonds*

153

after him, the DOG *leaps
from behind the trunk of
the* OAK *and, elbowing his
way through* TREES *and*
ANIMALS, *flings himself
before* TYLTYL, *whom he
defends furiously.*)

THE DOG (*distributing great bites*)

Here! Here, my little god! . . . Don't
be afraid! Have at them! . . . I
know how to use my teeth! . . .
Here, there's one for you, Bear, in
your fat hams! . . . Now then, who
wants some more? . . . Here, that's
for the Pig and that's for the Horse
and that's for the Bull's tail! . . .
There, I've torn the Beech's trousers
and the Oak's petticoat! . . . The
Fir-tree's making tracks! . . . Whew,
it's warm work! . . .

TYLTYL (*overcome*)

I'm done for! . . . The Cypress has
caught me a great blow on the
head.. . .

154

The Blue Bird

THE DOG

Ow! . . . That's the Willow! . . . He's
broken my paw! . . .

TYLTYL

They're coming back, they're charging
down upon us, all together! . . . This
time, it's the Wolf! . . .

THE DOG

Wait till I give him one for himself! . . .

THE WOLF

Fool! . . . Our brother! . . . His father
drowned your seven puppies! . . .

THE DOG

Quite right! . . . And a good thing too!
. . . It was because they looked like
you! . . .

ALL THE TREES AND ANIMALS

Renegade! . . . Idiot! . . . Traitor! . . .
Felon! . . . Simpleton! . . . Judas!
. . . Leave him! . . . He's a dead
man! . . . Come over to us! . . .

THE DOG (*drunk with ardour and devotion*)

Never! Never! . . . I alone against all
of you! . . . Never! Never! . . .

True to the gods, to the best, to the greatest! . . . (*To* TYLTYL) Take care, here's the Bear! . . . Beware of the Bull! . . . I'll jump at his throat. . . . Ow! . . . That's a kick. . . . The Ass has broken two of my teeth. . . .

TYLTYL

I'm done for, Tylô! . . . Ah! . . . That was a blow from the Elm. . . . Look, my hand's bleeding. . . . That's the Wolf or the Pig. . . .

THE DOG

Wait, my little god. . . . Let me kiss you. . . . There, a good lick. . . . That will do you good. . . . Keep behind me. . . . They dare not come again. . . . Yes, though. . . . Here they are coming back! . . . This time, it's serious! . . . We must stand firm! . . .

TYLTYL (*dropping to the ground*)

No, I can hold out no longer! . . .

THE DOG (*listening*)

They are coming! . . . I hear them, I scent them! . . .

156

The Blue Bird

TYLTYL

Where? . . . Who? . . .

THE DOG

There! There! . . . It's Light! . . . She
has found us! . . . Saved, my little
king! . . . Kiss me! . . . We are
saved! . . . Look! . . . They're
alarmed! . . . They're retreating!
. . . They're afraid! . . .

TYLTYL

Light! . . . Light! . . . Come quick!
. . . Hurry! . . . They have re-
belled! . . . They are all against
us! . . .

Enter LIGHT. *As she comes forward,
the dawn rises over the forest, which
becomes light.*

LIGHT

What is it? . . . What has happened?
. . . But, my poor boy, didn't you
know? . . . Turn the diamond! . . .
They will return into silence and ob-
scurity; and you will no longer perceive their hidden feelings. . . .

157

(TYLTYL *turns the diamond. Immediately, the souls of all the* TREES *rush back into the trunks, which close again. The souls of the* ANIMALS *also disappear; and a peaceful* COW *and* SHEEP, *etc., are seen browsing in the distance. The Forest becomes harmless once more.* TYLTYL *looks around him in amazement.*)

TYLTYL

Where are they? . . . What was the matter with them? . . . Were they mad? . . .

LIGHT

No, they are always like that; but we do not know it because we do not see it. . . . I told you so before; it is dangerous to wake them when I am not there. . . .

TYLTYL (*wiping his knife*)

Well, but for the Dog and if I had not had my knife! . . . I would never have believed that they were so wicked! . . .

dren should they be obliged to fly?
. . . .

THE DOG

Not at all! Not at all! I mean to go
everywhere with my little gods! Let
those who are afraid remain at the
door! We have no need (*looking at*
BREAD) of cowards (*looking at the*
CAT) or traitors! . . .

FIRE

I'm going! . . . I hear it's great fun!
. . . They dance all the time. . . .

BREAD

Do they have any eating as well?

WATER (*moaning*)

I have never known the smallest Happiness! . . . I should like to see some
at last! . . . .

LIGHT

Hold your tongues! Who asked your
opinions? . . . This is what I have
decided: the Dog, Bread and Sugar
shall go with the children. Water
shall stay outside, because she is too
cold, and Fire, because he is too tur-

163

bulent. I strongly urge Milk to remain at the door, because he is so impressionable. As for the Cat, he can do as he likes. . . . .

The Cat

I shall take the opportunity of calling on the chief Miseries of my acquaintance, who live next door to the Joys. . . .

Tyltyl

And you, Light? Aren't you coming?

Light

I cannot go into the Joys like this: most of them cannot endure me. But I have here the thick veil with which I cover myself when I visit happy people. . . . (*She unfolds a long veil and wraps herself in it carefully.*) Not a ray of my soul must startle them, for there are many Happinesses that are afraid and are not happy. . . . There . . . like this, even the ugliest and coarsest of them will have nothing to fear. . . .

(*The curtain opens and discloses the next Scene*)

The Blue Bird

SCENE 2.—*The Palace of Happiness*

*When the curtain of clouds opens, the stage
represents, in the forefront of the
palace, a sort of hall formed of tall
marble columns, between which hang
heavy purple draperies, supported by
golden ropes and concealing all the
background. The architecture suggests the most sensual and sumptuous
moments of the Venetian or Flemish
Renascence, as seen in the pictures of
Veronese or Rubens, with garlands,
horns of plenty, fringes, vases, statues,
gildings, lavishly distributed on every
side. In the middle stands a massive
and marvellous table of jasper and
silver-gilt, laden with candlesticks,
glass, gold and silver plate and fabu-
lous viands. Around the table, the
biggest luxuries of the Earth sit eating,
drinking, shouting, singing, tossing
and lolling about or sleeping among
the haunches of venison, the miracu-
lous fruits, the overturned jars and
ewers. They are enormously, incredi-*

165

*bly fat and red in the face, covered
with velvet and brocade, crowned with
gold and pearls and precious stones.
Beautiful female slaves incessantly
bring decorated dishes and foaming
beverages. Vulgar, blatantly hilarious
music, in which the brasses predomi-
nate. The stage is bathed in a red and
heavy light.*

(TYLTYL, MYTYL, *the* DOG, BREAD *and*
SUGAR *are a little awestruck at first
and crowd round* LIGHT *in the foreground, to the right. The* CAT, *without a word, walks to the background,
also to the right, lifts a dark curtain
and disappears.*)

TYLTYL

Who are those fat gentlemen enjoying
themselves and eating such a lot of
good things?

LIGHT

They are the biggest Luxuries of the Earth,
the ones that can be seen with the
naked eye. It is possible, though not

very likely, that the Blue Bird may have strayed among them for a moment. That is why you must not turn the diamond yet. For form's sake, we will begin by searching this part of the hall.

TYLTYL

Can we go up to them?

LIGHT

Certainly. They are not ill-natured, although they are vulgar and usually rather ill-bred.

MYTYL

What beautiful cakes they have! . . . .

THE DOG

And such game! And sausages! And legs of lamb and calves' liver! . . . There is nothing nicer or lovelier in the world than liver! . . .

BREAD

Except quartern-loaves made of fine white flour! They have splendid ones! . . . How lovely they are! How lovely they are! . . .

SUGAR

I beg your pardon, I beg your pardon, I
beg a thousand pardons. . . . Allow
me, allow me. . . . I would not like
to hurt anybody's feelings; but are you
not forgetting the sweetmeats, which
form the glory of that table and
which, if I may say so, surpass in
grandeur and magnificence all that
exists in this hall, or perhaps anywhere
else? . . .

TYLTYL

How pleased and happy they look! . . .
And they are shouting! And laughing! And singing! . . . I believe
they have seen us. . . .

(*A dozen of the biggest* LUX-
URIES *have risen from table
and now, holding their
stomachs in their hands, ad-
vance laboriously towards
the* CHILDREN.)

LIGHT

Have no fear, they are very affable. . . .
They will probably invite you to din-

ner. . . . Do not accept, do not accept anything, lest you should forget your mission. . . .

TYLTYL

What? Not even a tiny cake? They look so good, so fresh, so well iced with sugar, covered with candied fruits and brimming over with cream! . . .

LIGHT

They are dangerous and would break your will. A man should know how to sacrifice something to the duty he is performing. Refuse politely, but firmly.

THE BIGGEST OF THE LUXURIES (*holding out his hand to* TYLTYL)

How do you do, Tyltyl? . . .

TYLTYL (*surprised*)

Why, do you know me? . . . Who **are** you? . . .

THE LUXURY

I am the biggest of the Luxuries, the Luxury of Being Rich; and I come, in the name of my brothers, to beg you and your family to honour our endless repast with your presence. You will find yourself surrounded by all that is best among the real, big Luxuries of this Earth. Allow me to introduce to you the chief of them. Here is my son-in-law, the Luxury of Being a Landowner, who has a stomach shaped like a pear. This is the Luxury of Satisfied Vanity, who has such a nice, puffy face. (*The* LUXURY OF SATIS-FIED VANITY *gives a patronising nod*.) These are the Luxury of Drinking when you are not Thirsty and the Luxury of Eating when you are not Hungry: they are twins and their legs are made of macaroni. (*They bow, staggering*.) Here are the Luxury of Knowing Nothing, who is as deaf as a post, and the Luxury of Understanding Nothing, who is as blind as a bat. Here are the Luxury of Doing Nothing and the Luxury of Sleeping more than Necessary: their hands are made of bread-crumb and their eyes of peach-jelly. Lastly, here is Fat Laughter: his mouth is split from ear to ear and he is irresistible. . . . (FAT LAUGHTER *bows, writhing and holding his sides.*)

TYLTYL (*pointing to a* LUXURY *who is standing a little on one side*)

And who is that one, who dares not come up to us and who is turning his back? . . .

THE LUXURY OF BEING RICH

Do not ask about him: he is a little awkward and is not fit to be introduced to children. . . . (*Seizing* TYLTYL'S *hands*) But come along! They are beginning the banquet all over again. . . . It is the twelfth time since this morning. We are only waiting for you. . . . Do you hear all the revellers calling and shouting for you? . . . I cannot introduce you to all of them, there are so many of them. . . . (*Offering his arm to the two children*) Allow me to lead you to the two seats of honour. . . .

The Blue Bird

TYLTYL

No, thank you very much, Mr. Luxury.
. . . I am so sorry. . . . I can't
come for the moment. . . . We are
in a great hurry, we are looking for
the Blue Bird. You don't happen to
know, I suppose, where he is hiding?
. . .

THE LUXURY

The Blue Bird? . . . . Wait a bit. . . .
Yes, I remember. . . . Some one was
telling me about him the other day.
. . . He is a bird that is not good to
eat, I believe. . . . At any rate, he
has never figured on our table. . . .
That means that we have a poor opin-
ion of him. But don't trouble; we
have much better things. . . . You
shall share our life, you shall see all
that we do. . . .

TYLTYL

What do you do?

THE LUXURY

Why, we occupy ourselves incessantly in
doing nothing. . . . We never have a

moment's rest. . . . We have to drink, we have to eat, we have to sleep. It's most engrossing. . . .

TYLTYL

Is it amusing?

THE LUXURY

Why, yes. . . . It needs must be; it's all there is on this Earth. . . .

LIGHT

Do you think so?. . .

THE LUXURY (*pointing to* LIGHT, *aside, to* TYLTYL)

Who is that ill-bred young person? . . .

> (*During the whole of the preceding conversation, a crowd of* LUXURIES *of the second order have been busying themselves with the* DOG, SUGAR *and* BREAD *and have dragged them to the orgie.* TYLTYL *suddenly sees them seated fraternally at the table with their hosts, eating, drinking and flinging themselves about wildly.*)

173

The Blue Bird

TYLTYL

Why, look, Light! . . . They are sitting
at the table! . . .

LIGHT

Call them back, or this will have a bad
end! . . .

TYLTYL

Tylô! . . . Here, Tylô! . . . Come here
at once, will you? Do you hear? . . .
And you too, Sugar and Bread, who
told you to leave me? . . . What are
you doing there, without permission?

BREAD (*speaking with his mouth full*)

Can't you keep a civil tongue in your
mouth? . . .

TYLTYL

What? Is Bread daring to be imperti-
nent? . . . Why, what's come over
you? . . . And you, Tylô? . . . Is
that the way you obey? Now then,
come here, on your knees, on your
knees! . . . And look sharp! . . .

THE DOG (*muttering, from the end of the
table*)

When I'm eating, I'm at home to nobody
    and I hear nothing. . . .

        SUGAR (*honey-mouthed*)

Pardon us, we could not possibly leave such
    charming hosts so abruptly: they
    would be offended. . . .

        THE LUXURY

You see! . . . They are setting you an
    example. . . . Come, we are waiting
    for you. . . . We won't hear of a re-
    fusal. . . . We shall have to resort
    to a gentle violence. . . . Come, you
    Luxuries, help me! . . . Let us push
    them to the table by force, so that
    they may be happy in spite of them-
    selves! . . . (*All the* LUXURIES, *ut-
    tering cries of joy and skipping about
    as nimbly as they are able, drag the*
    CHILDREN, *who struggle, while* FAT
    LAUGHTER *seizes* LIGHT *vigorously
    round the waist.*)

        LIGHT

Turn the diamond, it is time! . . .

        (TYLTYL *obeys* LIGHT'S *order.
        Forthwith, the stage is lit*

up with an ineffably pure,
divinely roseate, harmonious
and ethereal brightness. The
heavy ornaments in the foreground, the thick red hang-
ings become unfastened and
disappear, revealing an immense and magnificent hall,
a sort of cathedral of glad-
ness and serenity, tall, innocent and almost transparent,
whose endless fabric rests
upon innumerous long and
slender, limpid and blissful
columns, suggesting the
architecture of the Palladian
churches or certain draw-
ings by Carpaccio, notably
the "Presentation of the
Virgin" in the Uffizi Gal-
lery. The table of the orgie
melts away without leaving
a trace; the velvets, the bro-
cades, the garlands of the
LUXURIES rise before the

luminous gust that invades the temple, tear asunder and fall, together with the grinning masks, at the feet of the astounded revellers. These become visibly deflated, like burst bladders, exchange glances, blink their eyes in the unknown rays that hurt them; and, seeing themselves at last as they really are, that is to say, naked, hideous, flabby and lamentable, they begin to utter yells of shame and dismay, amid which those of Fat Laughter *are clearly distinguishable above all the rest. The* Luxury of Understanding Nothing *alone remains perfectly calm, while his friends rush about madly, trying to flee, to hide themselves in corners which they hope to find dark. But there is not a shadow left in the dazzling room. And so the majority, in their despair, decide to pass through the threatening curtain which, in an angle on the right, closes the vault of the Cave of Miseries. Each time that one of them, in his panic, raises a skirt of the curtain, a storm of oaths, imprecations and maledictions is heard to issue from the hollow depths of the cave. As for the* Dog, Bread *and* Sugar, *they hang their heads, join the group of the* Children *and hide behind them very sheepishly.*)

Tyltyl (*watching the* Luxuries *flying*)
Goodness, how ugly they are! . . . Where are they going? . . .

Light

I really believe that they have lost their

heads. . . . They are going to take refuge with the Miseries, where I very much fear that they will be kept for good. . . .

TYLTYL (*looking around him, wonder-struck*)

Oh, what a beautiful hall, what a beautiful hall! . . . Where are we? . . .

LIGHT

We have not moved: it is your eyes that see differently. . . . We now behold the truth of things; and we shall perceive the soul of the Joys that endure the brightness of the diamond.

TYLTYL

How beautiful it is! . . . And what lovely weather! . . . It is just like midsummer. . . . Hullo! It looks as though people were coming to talk to us. . . .

(*The halls begin to fill with angel forms that seem to be emerging from a long slumber and glide harmoniously between the columns. They are clad in shimmering*

179

dresses, of soft and subtle
shades: rose - awakening,
water's - smile, amber - dew,
blue-of-dawn, etc.

LIGHT

Here come some amiable and curious Joys
who will direct us. . . .

TYLTYL

Do you know them? . . .

LIGHT

Yes, I know them all; I often come to
them, without their knowing who I
am. . . .

TYLTYL

Oh, what a lot of them there are! . . .
They are crowding from every side!
. . .

LIGHT

There were many more of them once.
The Luxuries have done them great
harm.

TYLTYL

No matter, there are a good few of them
left. . . .

LIGHT

You will see plenty of others, as the influence of the diamond spreads through the halls. . . . There are many more Happinesses on Earth than people think; but the generality of men do not discover them. . . .

TYLTYL

Here are some little ones: let us run and meet them. . . .

LIGHT

It is unnecessary: those which interest us will pass this way. We have no time to make the acquaintance of all the rest. . . .

> (*A troop of little* HAPPINESSES,
> *frisking and bursting with
> laughter, run up from the
> back of the halls and dance
> round the* CHILDREN *in a
> ring.*)

TYLTYL

How pretty, how very pretty they are!
. . . Where do they come from, who are they? . . .

The Blue Bird

LIGHT

They are the Children's Happinesses. . . .

TYLTYL

Can one speak to them?

LIGHT

It would be no use. They sing, they dance,
they laugh, but they do not talk
yet. . . .

TYLTYL (*skipping about*)

How do you do? How do you do? . . .
Oh, look at that fat one laughing!
. . . What pretty cheeks they have,
what pretty frocks they have! . . .
Are they all rich here? . . .

LIGHT

Why, no, here, as everywhere, there are
many more poor than rich. . . .

TYLTYL

Where are the poor ones? . . .

LIGHT

You can't distinguish them. . . . A
Child's Happiness is always arrayed
in all that is most beautiful in
Heaven and upon Earth.

182

The Blue Bird

TYLTYL (*unable to restrain himself*)
I should like to dance with them. . . .

LIGHT

It is absolutely impossible, we have no
time. . . . I see that they have not
the Blue Bird. . . . Besides, they are
in a hurry: you see, they have already
passed. . . . They too have no time
to waste, for childhood is very short.
. . .

> (*Another troop of* HAPPI-
> NESSES, *a little taller than
> the last, rush into the hall,
> singing at the top of their
> voice, "There they are!
> There they are! They see
> us! They see us!" and
> dance a merry fling around
> the* CHILDREN, *at the end
> of which the one who ap-
> pears to be the chief of the
> little band goes up to* TYL-
> TYL *with hand out-
> stretched.*)

183

The Blue Bird

THE HAPPINESS

How do you do, Tyltyl? . . .

TYLTYL

Another one who knows me! . . . (*To*
LIGHT) I am getting known wherever
I go! . . . (*To the* HAPPINESS)
Who are you? . . .

THE HAPPINESS

Don't you recognise me? . . . I'll wager
that you don't recognise any one here!
. . .

TYLTYL (*a little embarrassed*)

Why, no. . . . I don't know. . . . I
don't remember seeing any of you.
. . .

THE HAPPINESS

There, do you hear? . . . I was sure of it!
. . . He has never seen us! . . .
(*All the other* HAPPINESSES *burst out
laughing*) Why, my dear Tyltyl, we
are the only things you do know! . . .
We are always around you! . . . We
eat, drink, wake up, breathe and live
with you! . . .

The Blue Bird

TYLTYL

Oh, yes, just so, I know, I remember. . . .
But I should like to know what your
names are. . . .

THE HAPPINESS

I can see that you know nothing. . . . I
am the chief of the Happinesses of
your home; and all these are the other
Happinesses that live there. . . .

TYLTYL

Then there are Happinesses in my home?
. . .

(*All the* HAPPINESSES *burst out laughing.*)

THE HAPPINESS

You heard him! . . . Are there Happinesses in his home! . . . Why, you
little wretch, it is crammed with Happinesses in every nook and cranny!
. . . We laugh, we sing, we create
enough joy to knock down the walls
and lift the roof; but, do what we
may, you see nothing and you hear
nothing. . . . I hope that, in future,
you will be a little more sensible. . . .
Meantime, you shall shake hands with

185

the more noteworthy of us. . . .
Then, when you reach home again,
you will recognise them more easily
and, at the end of a fine day, you will
know how to encourage them with a
smile, to thank them with a pleasant
word, for they really do all they can
to make your life easy and delightful.
. . . Let me introduce myself first:
the Happiness of Being Well, at your
service. . . . I am not the prettiest,
but I am the most important. Will you
know me again? . . . This is the
Happiness of Pure Air, who is almost
transparent. . . . Here is the Happiness of Loving one's Parents, who is
clad in grey and always a little sad,
because no one ever looks at him. . . .
Here are the Happiness of the Blue
Sky, who, of course, is dressed in blue,
and the Happiness of the Forest, who,
also of course, is clad in green: you
will see him every time you go to the
window. . . . Here, again, is the
good Happiness of Sunny Hours, who

The Blue Bird

is diamond-coloured, and this is the
Happiness of Spring, who is bright
emerald. . . .

TYLTYL

And are you as fine as that every day?

THE HAPPINESS OF BEING WELL

Why, yes, it is Sunday every day, in every
house, when people open their eyes.
. . . And then, when evening comes,
here is the Happiness of the Sunsets,
who is grander than all the kings in
the world and who is followed by the
Happiness of Seeing the Stars Rise,
who is gilded like a god of old. . . .
Then, when the weather breaks, here
are the Happiness of the Rain, who
is covered with pearls, and the Happiness of the Winter Fire, who opens his
beautiful purple mantle to frozen
hands. . . . And I have not mentioned
the best among us, because he is nearly
a brother of the great limpid Joys
whom you will see presently: his name
is the Happiness of Innocent
Thoughts, and he is the brightest of

187

us all. . . . And then here are. . . .
But really there are too many of
them! . . . We should never have
done; and I must first send word to
the Great Joys, who are right at the
back, near the gates of Heaven, and
who have not yet heard of your arrival. . . . I will send the Happiness
of Running Barefoot in the Dew, who
is the nimblest of us. . . . (*To the*
HAPPINESS OF RUNNING BAREFOOT
IN THE DEW, *who comes forward
capering*) Off you go! . . .

LIGHT (*to* TYLTYL)

In the meantime, you might enquire about
the Blue Bird. It is just possible that
the chief Happiness of your home
knows where he is. . . .

TYLTYL

Where is he? . . .

THE HAPPINESS

He doesn't know where the Blue Bird is!
. . . (*All the* HAPPINESSES OF THE
HOME *burst out laughing.*)

The Blue Bird

TYLTYL (*vexed*)

No, I do not know. . . . There's nothing to laugh at. . . . (*Fresh bursts of laughter.*)

THE HAPPINESS

Come, don't be angry . . . and let us be serious. . . . He doesn't know: well, what do you expect? He is no more absurd than the majority of men. . . . But little Happiness of Running Barefoot in the Dew has told the Great Joys and they are coming towards us. . . .

> (*Tall and beautiful angelic figures, clad in shimmering dresses, come slowly forward.*)

TYLTYL

How beautiful they are! . . . Why are they not laughing? . . . Are they not happy? . . .

LIGHT

It is not when one laughs that one is really happy. . . .

189

The Blue Bird

TYLTYL

Who are they? . . .

THE HAPPINESS

They are the Great Joys. . . .

TYLTYL

Do you know their names? . . .

THE HAPPINESS

Of course; we often play with them. . . .
Here, first of all, before the others, is
the Great Joy of Being Just, who
smiles each time an injustice is re-
paired. I am too young: I have never
seen her smile yet. Behind her is the
Joy of Being Good, who is the hap-
piest, but the saddest; and it is very
difficult to keep her from going to the
Miseries, whom she would like to con-
sole; for, if she left us, we should be
almost as miserable as the Miseries
themselves. On the right is the Joy
of Fame, next to the Joy of Thinking.
After her comes the Joy of Understanding, who is always looking for
her brother, the Luxury of Understanding Nothing. . . .

TYLTYL

But I have seen her brother! . . . He
went to the Miseries with the Big
Luxuries. . . .

THE HAPPINESS

I was certain of it. . . . He has turned
out badly; keeping evil company has
corrupted him entirely. . . . But do
not speak of it to his sister. She
would want to go and look for him
and we should lose one of our most
beautiful Joys. . . . Here, among the
greatest Joys, is the Joy of Seeing
what is Beautiful, who daily adds a
few rays to the light that reigns
amongst us. . . .

TYLTYL

And there, far away, far away, in the
golden clouds, the one whom I can
hardly see when I stand as high as I
can on tip-toe? . . .

THE HAPPINESS

That is the Great Joy of Loving. . . .
But, do what you will, you are ever

191

so much too small to see her alto-
gether. . . .

TYLTYL

And over there, right at the back, those
who are veiled and who do not come
near? . . .

THE HAPPINESS

Those are the Joys whom men do not yet
know. . . .

TYLTYL

What do the others want with us? . . .
Why are they standing aside? . . .

THE HAPPINESS

It is before a new Joy who is arriving, perhaps the purest that we have here.
. . .

TYLTYL

Who is it?

THE HAPPINESS

Don't you recognise her yet? . . . But
take a better look at her, open your
two eyes down to the very heart of
your soul! . . . She has seen you, she
has seen you! . . . She runs up to
you, holding out her arms! . . . It

192

here, I want to stay also, as long as
you remain. . . .

MATERNAL LOVE

But it's just the same thing: I am down
below, we are all down below. . . .
You have come up here only to realise
and to learn, once and for all, how to
see me when you see me down below.
. . . Do you understand, Tyltyl
dear? . . . You believe yourself in
Heaven; but Heaven is wherever you
and I kiss each other. . . . There are
not two mothers; and you have no
other. . . . Every child has only
one; and it is always the same one and
always the most beautiful; but you
have to know her and to know how to
look. . . . But how did you manage
to come up here and to find a road
for which men have been seeking ever
since they began to dwell upon the
Earth? . . .

TYLTYL (*pointing to* LIGHT, *who, discreetly, has drawn a little to one side*)
She brought me. . . .

MATERNAL LOVE

Who is she? . . .

TYLTYL

Light. . . .

MATERNAL LOVE

I have never seen her. . . . I was told that
she was very fond of you both and
very kind. . . . But why does she
hide herself? . . . Does she never
show her face? . . .

TYLTYL

Oh, yes, but she is afraid that the Joys
might be frightened if they saw too
clearly. . . .

MATERNAL LOVE

But doesn't she know that we are waiting
only for her! (*Calling the other*
GREAT JOYS) Come, come, sisters!
Come quickly, all of you! Light has
come to visit us at last! . . .

> (*A stir among the* GREAT JOYS,
> *who draw nearer, with cries*
> *of "Light is here! . . .*
> *Light! Light! . . ."*)

THE JOY OF UNDERSTANDING (*thrusting all the others aside, to come and embrace* LIGHT)

You are Light and we did not know it! . . . And we have been waiting for you for years and years and years! . . . Do you recognise me? . . . I am the Joy of Understanding, who have been seeking you for so long! . . . We are very happy, but we cannot see beyond ourselves. . . .

THE JOY OF BEING JUST (*embracing* LIGHT *in her turn*)

Do you recognise me? . . . I am the Joy of Being Just, who have besought you so long. . . . We are very happy, but we cannot see beyond our shadows. . . .

THE JOY OF SEEING WHAT IS BEAUTIFUL (*also embracing* LIGHT)

Do you recognise me? . . . I am the Joy of Seeing what is Beautiful, who have loved you so dearly. . . . We are very happy, but we cannot see beyond our dreams. . . .

199

The Blue Bird

The Joy of Understanding

Come, sister, come, do not keep us waiting
   any longer. . . . We are strong
   enough, we are pure enough. . . .
   Put aside those veils which still conceal from us the last truths and the
   last happinesses. . . . See, all my sisters are kneeling at your feet. . . .
   You are our queen and our reward.
   . . .

Light (*drawing her veils closer*)

Sisters, my beautiful sisters, I am obeying
   my Master. . . . The hour is not yet
   come; it will strike, perhaps, and I
   shall return without fear and without
   shadow. . . . Farewell, rise and let
   us kiss once more, like sisters lost and
   found, while waiting for the day that
   will soon appear. . . .

Maternal Love (*embracing* Light)

You have been very good to my poor little
   ones. . . .

Light

I shall always be good to those who love
   one another. . . .

The Blue Bird

THE JOY OF UNDERSTANDING (*going up
to* LIGHT)
Let the last kiss be laid upon my forehead.
    . . .

> (*They exchange a long kiss; and,
> when they separate and
> raise their heads, tears are
> seen to stand in their eyes.*)

TYLTYL (*surprised*)
Why are you crying? . . . (*Looking at
the other* JOYS) I say! You're crying
too! . . . But why have all of you
tears in your eyes? . . .

LIGHT
Hush, dear. . . .

CURTAIN

The Blue Bird

Act V

Scene 1.—*Before the Curtain.*

Enter Tyltyl, Mytyl, Light, *the* Dog, *the* Cat, Bread, Fire, Sugar, Water *and* Milk.

Light

I have received a note from the Fairy Bérylune telling me that the Blue Bird is probably here.

Tyltyl

Where? . . .

Light

Here, in the graveyard behind that wall. . . . It appears that one of the dead in the graveyard is hiding it in his tomb. . . . We must find out which one it is. . . . We shall have to pass them under review. . . .

Tyltyl

Under review? . . . How is that done? . . .

Light

It is very simple: at midnight, so as not to

203

disturb them too greatly, you will turn
the diamond. We shall see them
come out of the ground; or else we
shall see those who do not come out ly-
ing in their tombs. . . .

TYLTYL

Will they not be angry? . . .

LIGHT

Not at all; they will not even know. . . .
They do not like being disturbed, but,
as it is their custom, in any case, to
come out at midnight, that will not in-
convenience them. . . .

TYLTYL

Why are Bread, Sugar and Milk so pale
and why do they say nothing? . . .

MILK (*staggering*)

I feel I am going to turn. . . .

LIGHT (*aside to* TYLTYL)

Do not mind them. . . . They are afraid
of the dead. . . .

FIRE (*frisking about*)

I'm not afraid of them! . . . I am used to
burning them. . . . Time was when I

burnt them all; that was much more
amusing than nowadays. . . .

TYLTYL

And why is Tylô trembling? . . . Is he
afraid, too? . . .

THE DOG

I? . . . I'm not trembling! . . . I am
never afraid; but if you went away,
I should go too. . . .

TYLTYL

And has the Cat nothing to say? . . .

THE CAT (*mysteriously*)

I know what's what. . . .

TYLTYL (*to* LIGHT)

Are you coming with us? . . .

LIGHT

No; it is better that I should remain at the
gate of the graveyard with the Things
and the Animals. . . . Some of them
would be too frightened and I fear
that the others would misbehave. . . .
Fire, in particular, would want to burn
the dead, as of old; and that is no
longer done. . . . I shall leave you
alone with Mytyl. . . .

The Blue Bird

TYLTYL

And may not Tylô stay with us? . . .

THE DOG

Yes, yes, I shall stay; I shall stay here! . . .
I want to stay with my little god! . . .

LIGHT

It is impossible. . . . The Fairy gave
formal orders; besides, there is nothing to fear. . . .

THE DOG

Very well, very well, it makes no difference.
If they are vicious, my little god, all
you have to do is this . . . (*he
whistles*) and you shall see. . . . It
will be just as in the forest: Wow!
Wow! Wow! . . .

LIGHT

Come, good-bye, dear children. . . . I shall
not be far away. . . . (*She kisses the*
CHILDREN.) Those who love me and
whom I love always find me again. . . .
(*To the* THINGS *and the* ANIMALS)
This way, all of you. . . .

(*She goes out with the* THINGS
and the ANIMALS. *The*
206

Children remain alone in the middle of the stage. The curtain opens and discloses the next scene.)

Scene 2.—*The Graveyard.*

It is night. The moon is shining on a country graveyard.. Numerous tombstones, grassy mounds, wooden crosses, stone slabs, etc. Tyltyl and Mytyl are standing by a short stone pillar.

Mytyl

I am frightened! . . .

Tyltyl (*not too much at his ease*)

I am never frightened. . . .

Mytyl

I say, are the dead wicked? . . .

Tyltyl

Why, no, they're not alive! . . .

Mytyl

Have you ever seen one? . . .

Tyltyl

Yes, once, long ago, when I was very young. . . .

207

MYTYL

What was it like, say? . . .

TYLTYL

Quite white, very still and very cold and it
didn't talk. . . .

MYTYL

Are we going to see them, say? . . .

TYLTYL

Why, of course, Light said so. . . .

MYTYL

Where are they? . . .

TYLTYL

Here, under the grass or under those big
stones. . . .

MYTYL

Are they there all the year round? . . .

TYLTYL

Yes.

MYTYL (*pointing to the slabs*)

Are those the doors of their houses? . . [o]

TYLTYL

Yes.

MYTYL

Do they go out when it's fine? . . .

The Blue Bird

TYLTYL

They can only go out at night. . . .

MYTYL

Why? . . .

TYLTYL

Because they are in their shirts. . . .

MYTYL

Do they go out also when it rains? . . .

TYLTYL

When it rains, they stay at home. . . .

MYTYL

Is it nice in their homes, say? . . .

TYLTYL

They say it's very cramped. . . .

MYTYL

Have they any little children? . . .

TYLTYL

Why, yes; they have all those that die. . .

MYTYL

And what do they live on? . . .

TYLTYL

They eat roots. . . .

MYTYL

Shall we see them? . . .

209

TYLTYL

Of course; we see everything when I turn the diamond.

MYTYL

And what will they say? . . .

TYLTYL

They will say nothing, as they don't talk. . . .

MYTYL

Why don't they talk? . . .

TYLTYL

Because they have nothing to say. . . .

MYTYL

Why have they nothing to say? . . .

TYLTYL

You're a nuisance. . . .

(*A pause*)

MYTYL

When will you turn the diamond?

TYLTYL

You heard Light say that I was to wait until midnight, because that disturbs them less. . . .

MYTYL

Why does that disturb them less? . . .

TYLTYL

Because that is when they go out to take the
air. . . .

MYTYL

Is it not midnight yet? . . .

TYLTYL

Do you see the church clock? . . .

MYTYL

Yes, I can even see the small hand. . . .

TYLTYL

Well, midnight is just going to strike. . . .
There! . . . Do you hear? . . .

(*The clock strikes twelve*)

MYTYL

I want to go away! . . .

TYLTYL

Not now. . . . I am going to turn the diamond. . . .

MYTYL

No, no! . . . Don't! . . . I want to go
away! . . . I am so frightened, little
brother! . . . I am terribly frightened! . . .

TYLTYL

But there is no danger. . . .

MYTYL

I don't want to see the dead! . . . I don't
want to see them! . . .

TYLTYL

Very well, you shall not see them; shut your
eyes. . . .

MYTYL (*clinging to* TYLTYL'S *clothes*)

Tyltyl, I can't stay! . . . No, I can't possibly! . . . They are going to come
out of the ground! . . .

TYLTYL

Don't tremble like that. . . . They will
only come out for a moment. . . .

MYTYL

But you're trembling, too! . . . They will
be awful! . . .

TYLTYL

It is time, the hour is passing. . . .

> (TYLTYL *turns the diamond. A
> terrifying minute of silence
> and motionlessness elapses,
> after which, slowly, the
> crosses totter, the mounds
> open, the slabs rise up. . . .*)

MYTYL (*cowering against* TYLTYL)
They are coming out! . . . They are
   there! . . .

> (*Then, from all the gaping
> tombs, there rises gradually
> an efflorescence at first frail
> and timid, like steam; then
> white and virginal and
> more and more tufty, more
> and more tall and plentiful
> and marvellous. Little by
> little, irresistibly, invading
> all things, it transforms the
> graveyard into a sort of
> fairy-like and nuptial gar-
> den, over which rise the first
> rays of the dawn. The dew
> glitters, the flowers open
> their blooms, the wind mur-
> murs in the leaves, the bees
> hum, the birds wake and
> flood the air with the first
> raptures of their hymns to
> the sun and to life. Stunned
> and dazzled.* TYLTYL *and*

213

MYTYL, *holding each other by the hand, take a few steps among the flowers while they seek for the trace of the tombs.*)

MYTYL (*looking in the grass*)

Where are the dead? . . .

TYLTYL (*looking also*)

There are no dead. . . .

CURTAIN

SCENE 3.—*The Kingdom of the Future.*

The immense halls of the Azure Palace, where the children wait that are yet to be born. Infinite perspectives of sapphire columns supporting turquoise vaults. Everything, from the light and the lapis-lazuli flagstones to the shimmering background into which the last arches run and disappear, everything, down to the smallest objects, is of an unreal, intense, fairy-like blue. Only the plinths and capitals of the columns, the key-stones, a few seats

214

and circular benches are of white mar-
ble or alabaster. To the right, be-
tween the columns, are great opales-
cent doors. These doors, which TIME
will throw back towards the end of the
scene, open upon actual life and the
quays of the Dawn. Everywhere,
harmoniously peopling the hall, is a
crowd of CHILDREN *robed in long*
azure garments. Some are playing,
others strolling to and fro, others talk-
ing or dreaming; many are asleep,
many also are working, between the
colonnades, at future inventions; and
their tools, their instruments, the ap-
paratus which they are constructing,
the plants, flowers and fruit which
they are cultivating or plucking are of
the same supernatural and luminous
blue as the general atmosphere of the
Palace. Figures of a taller stature,
clad in a paler and more diaphanous
azure, figures of a sovereign and silent
beauty move among the CHILDREN
and would seem to be angels.

215

Enter on the left, as though by stealth, gliding between the columns in the foreground, TYLTYL, MYTYL *and* LIGHT. *Their arrival causes a certain movement among the* BLUE CHILDREN, *who come running up on every hand, form a group around the unwonted visitors and gaze upon them with curiosity.*

MYTYL

Where are Sugar, the Cat and Bread? . . .

LIGHT

They cannot enter here; they would know the future and would not obey. . . .

TYLTYL

And the Dog? . . .

LIGHT

It is not well, either, that he should know what awaits him in the course of the ages. . . . I have locked them all up in the vaults of the church. . . .

TYLTYL

Where are we? . . .

LIGHT

We are in the Kingdom of the Future, in

216

the midst of the children who are not
yet born.   As the diamond allows us
to see clearly in this region which is
hidden from men, we shall very probably find the Blue Bird here. . . .

Tyltyl

Certainly the bird will be blue, since everything here is blue. . . . (*Looking all
around him.*) Heaven, how beautiful
it all is! . . .

Light

Look at the children running up. . . .

Tyltyl

Are they angry? . . .

Light

Not at all. . . . You can see, they are
smiling, but they are surprised. . . .

The Blue Children (*running up in ever-increasing numbers*)

Live children! . . . Come and look at the
little live children! . . .

Tyltyl

Why do they call us the little live children?

LIGHT

Because they themselves are not alive
yet. . . .

TYLTYL

What are they doing, then? . . .

LIGHT

They are awaiting the hour of their
birth. . . .

TYLTYL

The hour of their birth? . . .

LIGHT

Yes; it is from here that all the children
come who are born upon our earth.
Each awaits his day. . . . When the
fathers and mothers want children,
the great doors which you see there,
on the right, are opened and the little
ones go down. . . .

TYLTYL

What a lot there are! What a lot there
are! . . .

LIGHT

There are many more. . . . We do not see
them all. . . . There are thirty
thousand halls like this, all full of

them. . . . Just think, there are enough to last to the end of the world! . . . No one could count them. . . .

TYLTYL

And those tall blue persons, who are they? . . .

LIGHT

No one exactly knows. . . . They are believed to be guardians. . . . I have heard that they will come upon earth after men. . . . But we are not allowed to ask them. . . .

TYLTYL

Why not? . . .

LIGHT

Because it is the earth's secret. . . .

TYLTYL

And may one talk to the others, the little ones? . . .

LIGHT

Certainly; you must make friends. . . . Look, there is one who is more curious than the rest. . . . Go up to him, speak to him. . . .

The Blue Bird

TYLTYL

What shall I say to him? . . .

LIGHT

Whatever you like, as you would to a little
    playfellow. . . .

TYLTYL

Can I shake hands with him? . . .

LIGHT

Of course, he won't hurt you. . . .
    But come, don't look so constrained.
    . . . I will leave you alone, you will
    be more at ease by yourselves. . . .
    Besides, I want to speak to the tall
    blue person. . . .

TYLTYL (*going up to the* BLUE CHILD
    and holding out his hand)

How do you do? . . . (*Touching the*
    CHILD'S *blue dress with his finger.*)
    What's that? . . .

THE CHILD (*gravely touching* TYLTYL'S
    hat)

And that? . . .

TYLTYL

That? . . . That is my hat. . . . Have
    you no hat? . . .

The Blue Bird

THE CHILD

No; what is it for? . . .

TYLTYL

It's to say How-do-you-do with. . . . And
then for when it rains or when it's
cold. . . .

THE CHILD

What does that mean, when it's cold? . . .

TYLTYL

When you shiver like this: brrrr! brrrr!
. . . When you blow into your hands
and go like this with your arms. . . .
(*He vigorously beats his arms across
his chest.*)

THE CHILD

Is it cold on earth? . . .

TYLTYL

Yes, sometimes, in the winter, when there
is no fire. . . .

THE CHILD

Why is there no fire? . . .

TYLTYL

Because it's expensive and it costs money
to buy wood. . . .

221

THE CHILD

What is money? . . .

TYLTYL

It's what you pay with. . . .

THE CHILD

Oh. . . .

TYLTYL

Some people have money and others have
none. . . .

THE CHILD

Why not? . . .

TYLTYL

Because they are not rich. . . . Are you
rich? . . . How old are you? . . .

THE CHILD

I am going to be born soon. . . . I shall
be born in twelve years. . . . Is it
nice to be born? . . .

TYLTYL

Oh, yes! . . . It's great fun! . . .

THE CHILD

How did you manage? . . .

TYLTYL

I can't remember. . . . It is so long
ago! . . .

222

THE CHILD

They say it's lovely, the earth and the live
    people! . . .

TYLTYL

Yes, it's not bad. . . . There are birds and
    cakes and toys. . . . Some have them
    all; but those who have none can look
    at them. . . .

THE CHILD

They tell us that the mothers stand
    waiting at the door. . . . They are
    good, aren't they? . . .

TYLTYL

Oh, yes! . . . They are better than any-
    thing in the world! . . . And the
    grannies too; but they die too
    soon. . . .

THE CHILD

They die? . . . What is that? . . .

TYLTYL

They go away one evening and do not
    come back. . . .

THE CHILD

Why? . . .

TYLTYL

How can one tell? . . . Perhaps because
they feel sad. . . .

THE CHILD

Has yours gone? . . .

TYLTYL

My grandmamma? . . .

THE CHILD

Your mamma or your grandmamma, I
don't know. . . .

TYLTYL

Oh, but it's not the same thing! . . . The
grannies go first; that's sad enough.
. . . Mine was very kind to me. . . .

THE CHILD

What is the matter with your eyes? . . .
Are they making pearls? . . .

TYLTYL

No; it's not pearls. . . .

THE CHILD

What is it, then? . . .

TYLTYL

It's nothing; it's all that blue, which
dazzles me a little. . . .

The Blue Bird

THE CHILD

What is that called? . . .

TYLTYL

What? . . .

THE CHILD

There, that, falling down. . . .

TYLTYL

Nothing, it is a little water. . . .

THE CHILD

Does it come from the eyes? . . .

TYLTYL

Yes, sometimes, when one cries. . . .

THE CHILD

What does that mean, crying? . . .

TYLTYL

I have not been crying; it is the fault of
that blue. . . But if I had cried, it
would be the same thing. . . .

THE CHILD

Does one often cry? . . .

TYLTYL

Not little boys, but little girls do. . . .
Don't you cry here? . . .

THE CHILD

No; I don't know how. . . .

TYLTYL

Well, you will learn. . . . What are you
playing with, those great blue
wings? . . .

THE CHILD

These? . . . That's for the invention
which I shall make on earth. . . .

TYLTYL

What invention? . . . Have you invented
something? . . .

THE CHILD

Why, yes; have you heard? . . . When
I am on earth, I shall have to invent
the thing that gives happiness. . . .

TYLTYL

Is it good to eat? . . . Does it make a
noise? . . .

THE CHILD

No; you hear nothing. . . .

TYLTYL

That's a pity. . . .

THE CHILD

I work at it every day. . . . It is almost
finished. . . . Would you like to see
it? . . .

The Blue Bird

TYLTYL

Very much. . . . Where is it? . . .

THE CHILD

There, you can see it from here, between
those two columns. . . .

ANOTHER BLUE CHILD (*coming up to*
TYLTYL *and plucking his sleeve*)

Would you like to see mine, say? . . .

TYLTYL

Yes, what is it? . . .

THE SECOND CHILD

The thirty-three remedies for prolonging
life. . . . There, in those blue
phials. . . .

A THIRD CHILD (*stepping out from the
crowd*)

I will show you a light which nobody
knows of! . . . (*He lights himself
up entirely with an extraordinary
flame.*) It's rather curious, isn't
it? . . .

A FOURTH CHILD (*pulling* TYLTYL's
arm)

Do come and look at my machine which

flies in the air like a bird without wings! . . .

A FIFTH CHILD

No, no; mine first! It discovers the treasures hidden in the moon! . . .

THE BLUE CHILDREN (*crowding round* TYLTYL *and* MYTYL *and all crying together*)

No, no, come and see mine! . . . No, mine is much finer! . . . Mine is a wonderful invention! . . . Mine is made of sugar! . . . His is no good! . . . He stole the idea from me! . . .

> (*Amid these disordered exclamations, the* LIVE CHILDREN *are dragged towards the blue workshops, where each of the inventors sets his ideal machine going. There ensues a cerulean whirl of wheels, disks, flywheels, driving-wheels, pulleys, straps and strange and as yet unnamed objects shrouded in the bluey mists*

of the unreal. A crowd of odd and mysterious mechan-isms dart forth and hover under the vaults or crawl at the foot of the columns, while CHILDREN *unfold charts and plans, open books, uncover azure stat-ues and bring enormous flowers and gigantic fruits that seem formed of sap-phires and turquoises.*)

A LITTLE BLUE CHILD (*bending under the weight of some colossal blue daisies*)

Look at my flowers! . . .

TYLTYL

What are they? . . . I don't know them. . . .

THE LITTLE BLUE CHILD

They are daisies! . . .

TYLTYL

Impossible! . . . They are as big as tables! . . .

229

The Blue Bird

THE LITTLE BLUE CHILD

And they smell so good! . . .

TYLTYL (*smelling them*)

Wonderful! . . .

THE LITTLE BLUE CHILD

They will grow like that when I am on
earth. . . .

TYLTYL

When will that be? . . .

THE LITTLE BLUE CHILD

In fifty-three years, four months and nine
days. . . .

> (*Two* BLUE CHILDREN *arrive,
> carrying, like a lustre hang-
> ing on a pole, an incredible
> bunch of grapes, each larger
> than a pear.*)

ONE OF THE CHILDREN (*carrying the
grapes*)

What do you say to my fruits? . . .

TYLTYL

A bunch of pears! . . .

THE CHILD

No, they are grapes! . . . They will all

be like that when I am thirty. . . . I have found the way. . . .

ANOTHER CHILD (*staggering under a basket of blue apples the size of melons*)

And mine! . . . Look at my apples! . . .

TYLTYL

But those are melons! . . .

THE CHILD

No, no! . . . They are my apples and they are not the finest at that! . . . They will all be alike when I am alive. . . . I have discovered the system! . . .

ANOTHER CHILD (*wheeling a blue barrow with blue melons bigger than pumpkins*)

What do you say to my little melons? . . .

TYLTYL

But they are pumpkins! . . .

THE CHILD WITH THE MELONS

When I come on earth, the melons will be splendid! . . . I shall be the gardener of the King of the Three Planets. . . .

231

The Blue Bird

TYLTYL

The King of the Three Planets?

THE CHILD WITH THE MELONS

The great king who for thirty-five years
will bring happiness to the Earth,
Mars and the Moon. . . . You can
see him from here. . . .

TYLTYL

Where is he? . . .

THE CHILD WITH THE MELONS

There, the little boy sleeping at the foot of
that column.

TYLTYL

On the left? . . .

THE CHILD WITH THE MELONS

No, on the right. . . . The one on the left
is the child who will bring pure joy
to the globe. . . .

TYLTYL

How? . . .

THE CHILD (*the one that first talked to*
TYLTYL)

By means of ideas which people have not
yet had. . . .

TYLTYL

And the other, that little fat one with his
fingers to his nose, what will he
do? . . .

THE CHILD

He is to discover the fire that will warm
the earth when the sun is paler than
now. . . .

TYLTYL

And the two holding each other by the
hand and always kissing; are they
brother and sister? . . .

THE CHILD

No; they are very comical. . . . They are
the Lovers. . . .

TYLTYL

What is that? . . .

THE CHILD

I don't know. . . . Time calls them that,
to make fun of them. . . . They
spend the day looking into each
other's eyes, kissing and bidding each
other farewell. . . .

TYLTYL

Why? . . .

THE CHILD

It seems that they will not be able to leave together. . . .

TYLTYL

And the little pink one, who looks so serious and is sucking his thumb, what is he? . . .

THE CHILD

It appears that he is to wipe out injustice from the earth. . . .

TYLTYL

Oh! . . .

THE CHILD

They say it's a tremendous work. . . .

TYLTYL

And the little red-haired one, who walks as if he did not see where he was going, is he blind? . . .

THE CHILD

Not yet; but he will become so. . . . Look at him well; it seems that he is to conquer Death. . . .

TYLTYL

What does that mean? . . .

The Blue Bird

THE CHILD

I don't exactly know; but they say it's a
    great thing. . . .

TYLTYL (*pointing to a crowd of* CHIL-
    DREN *sleeping at the foot of the*
    columns, on the steps, the benches,
    etc.)

And all those asleep, what a number of
    them there are asleep! . . . Do they
    do nothing? . . .

THE CHILD

They are thinking of something. . . .

TYLTYL

Of what? . . .

THE CHILD

They do not know yet; but they must take
    something with them to earth; we
    are not allowed to go from here emp-
    ty-handed. . . .

TYLTYL

Who says so? . . .

THE CHILD

Time, who stands at the door. . . . You
    will see when he opens it. . . . He is
    very tiresome. . . .

A Child (*running up from the back of the hall and elbowing his way through the crowd*)

How are you, TYLTYL? . . .

TYLTYL

Hullo! . . . How does he know my name? . . .

THE CHILD (*who has just run up and who now kisses* TYLTYL *and* MYTYL *effusively.*)

How are you? . . . All right? . . . Come, give me a kiss, and you too, Mytyl. It's not surprising that I should know your name, seeing that I shall be your brother. . . . They have only just told me that you were here. . . . I was right at the other end of the hall, packing up my ideas. . . . Tell mummy that I am ready. . . .

TYLTYL

What? . . . Are you coming to us? . . .

THE CHILD

Certainly, next year, on Palm Sunday. . . . Don't tease me too much when I am little. . . . I am very glad to have

236

kissed you both beforehand. . . .
Tell daddy to mend the cradle. . . .
Is it comfortable in our home? . . .

Tyltyl

Not bad. . . . And mummy is so
kind! . . .

The Child

And the food? . . .

Tyltyl

That depends. . . . We even have cakes
sometimes, don't we, Mytyl? . . .

Mytyl

On New Year's Day and the fourteenth of
July. . . . Mummy makes them. . . .

Tyltyl

What have you got in that bag? . . . Are
you bringing us something? . . .

The Child

I am bringing three illnesses: scarlatina,
whooping-cough and measles. . . .

Tyltyl

Oh, that's all, is it? . . . And, after that,
what will you do? . . .

The Child

After that? . . . I shall leave you. . . .

TYLTYL

It will hardly be worth while coming! . . . .

THE CHILD

We can't pick and choose! . . .

> (*At that moment, a sort of prolonged, powerful, crystalline vibration is heard to rise and swell; it seems to emanate from the columns and the opal doors, which are irradiated by a brighter light than before.*)

TYLTYL

What is that? . . .

THE CHILD

That's Time! . . . He is going to open the gates! . . .

> (*A great change comes over the crowd of* BLUE CHILDREN. *Most of them leave their machines and their labours, numbers of sleepers awake and all turn their eyes towards the opal doors and go nearer to them.*)

238

LIGHT (*joining* TYLTYL)

Let us try to hide behind the columns. . . .
　　It will not do for Time to discover
　　us. . . .

TYLTYL

Where does that noise come from? . . .

A CHILD

It is the Dawn rising. . . . This is the
　　hour when the children who are to be
　　born to-day go down to earth. . . .

TYLTYL

How will they go down? . . . Are there
　　ladders? . . .

THE CHILD

You shall see. . . . Time is drawing the
　　bolts. . . .

TYLTYL

Who is Time? . . .

THE CHILD

An old man who comes to call those who
　　are going. . . .

TYLTYL

Is he wicked? . . .

THE CHILD

No; but he hears nothing. . . . **Beg as**

they may, if it's not their turn, he pushes back all those who try to go. . . .

TYLTYL

Are they glad to go? . . .

THE CHILD

We are sorry when we are left behind, but we are sad when we go. . . . There! There! . . . He is opening the doors! . . .

> (*The great opalescent doors turn slowly on their hinges. The sounds of the earth are heard like a distant mu-sic. A red and green light penetrates into the hall;* TIME, *a tall old man with a streaming beard, armed with his scythe and hour-glass, appears upon the threshold; and the spectator perceives the extremity of the white and gold sails of a galley moored to a sort of*

240

*quay, formed by the rosy
mists of the Dawn.*)

TIME (*on the threshold*)

Are they ready whose hour has struck?...

BLUE CHILDREN (*elbowing their way and
running up from all sides*)

Here we are! . . . Here we are! . . .
Here we are! . . .

TIME (*in a gruff voice to the* CHILDREN
defiling before him to go out)

One at a time! . . . Once again, there are
many more of you than are wanted!
. . . It's always the same thing! . . .
You can't deceive me! . . . (*Pushing
back a* CHILD.) It's not your turn!
. . . Go back and wait till to-morrow.
. . . Nor you either; go in and return in ten years. . . . A thirteenth
shepherd? . . . There are only twelve
wanted; there is no need for more; the
days of Theocritus and Virgil are past.
. . . More doctors? . . . There are
too many already; they are grumbling
about it on earth. . . . And where are
the engineers? . . . They want an

honest man, only one, as a phenome-
non. . . . Where is the honest man?
. . . Is it you? . . . (THE CHILD
nods yes.) You appear to me to be a
very poor specimen! . . . Hallo, you,
over there, not so fast, not so fast! . . .
And you, what are you bringing? . . .
Nothing at all, empty-handed? . . .
Then you can't go through. . . . Pre-
pare something, a great crime, if you
like, or a fine sickness, I don't care
. . . but you must have something. . . .
(*Catching sight of a little* CHILD
*whom the others are pushing forward,
while he resists with all his strength.*)
Well, what's the matter with you? . . .
You know that the hour has come. . . .
They want a hero to fight against injustice; you're the one; you must
start. . . .

THE BLUE CHILDREN

He doesn't want to, sir. . . .

TIME

What? . . . He doesn't want to? . . .
Where does the little monster think he

is? . . . No objections, we have no
time to spare. . . .

THE CHILD (*who is being pushed*)

No, no! . . . I don't want to go! . . . I
would rather not be born! . . . I
would rather stay here! . . .

TIME

That is not the question. . . . When the
hour comes, it comes! . . . Now then,
quick, forward! . . .

.   A CHILD (*stepping forward*)

Oh, let me pass! . . . I will go and take his
place! . . . They say that my parents
are old and have been waiting for me
so long! . . .

TIME

None of that! . . . You will start at your
proper hour, at your proper time. . . .
We should never be done if we lis-
tened to you. . . . One wants to go,
another refuses; it's too soon or it's too
late. . . . (*Pushing back some* CHIL-
DREN *who have encroached upon the
threshold.*) Not so near, you children! . . . Back, you inquisitive ones!

. . . Those who are not starting have
no business outside. . . . You are in a
hurry now; later, when your turn
comes, you will be frightened and
hang back. . . . Look, there are four
who are trembling like leaves. . . .
(*To a* CHILD *who, on the point of
crossing the threshold, suddenly goes
back.*) Well, what is it? . .. ...
What's the matter? . . .

THE CHILD

I have forgotten the box containing the two
crimes which I shall have to commit. . . .

ANOTHER CHILD

And I the little pot with my idea for en-
lightening the crowd. . . .

A THIRD CHILD

I have forgotten the graft of my finest
pear! . . .

TIME

Run quick and fetch them! . . . We have
only six hundred and twelve seconds
left. . . . The galley of the Dawn is already flapping her sails to show that

she is waiting. . . . You will come too
late and you won't be born! . . .
Come, quick, on board with you! . . .
(*Laying hold of a* CHILD *who tries to
pass between his legs to reach the
quay.*) Oh, no, not you! . . . This
is the third time you've tried to be
born before your turn. . . . Don't let
me catch you at it again, or you can
wait forever with my sister Eternity;
and you know that it's not amusing
there! . . . But come, are we ready?
. . . Is every one at his post? . . .
(*Surveying the* CHILDREN *standing
on the quay or already seated in the
galley.*) There is still one missing.
. . . It is no use his hiding, I see him
in the crowd. . . . You can't deceive
me! . . . Come on, you, the little fellow whom they call the Lover, say
good-bye to your sweetheart. . . .

(*The two* CHILDREN *who are
called the Lovers, fondly en-
twined, their faces livid*
245

with despair, go up to TIME
and kneel at his feet.)

THE FIRST CHILD

Mr. Time, let me stay behind with her! . . ,

THE SECOND CHILD

Mr. Time, let me go with him! . . .

TIME

Impossible! . . . We have only three hundred and ninety-four seconds left. . . .

THE FIRST CHILD

I would rather not be born! . . .

TIME

You cannot choose. . . .

THE SECOND CHILD (*beseechingly*)

Mr. Time, I shall come too late! . . .

THE FIRST CHILD

I shall be gone before she comes down! . . .

THE SECOND CHILD

I shall never see him again! . . .

THE FIRST CHILD

We shall be alone in the world! . . .

TIME

All this does not concern me. . . . Address your entreaties to Life. . . . I unite

and part as I am told. . . . (*Seizing
one of the* CHILDREN.) Come! . . .

THE FIRST CHILD (*struggling*)

No, no, no! . . . She, too! . . .

THE SECOND CHILD (*clinging to the
clothes of the* FIRST)

Leave him with me! . . . Leave him! . . .

TIME

Come, come, he is not going to die, but to
live! . . . (*Dragging away the* FIRST
CHILD.) Come along! . . .

THE SECOND CHILD (*stretching her arms
out frantically to the* CHILD *that is
being carried off*)

A sign! . . . A sign! . . . Tell me how to
find you! . . .

THE FIRST CHILD

I shall always love you! . . .

THE SECOND CHILD

I shall be the saddest thing on earth! . . .
You will know me by that! . . .
(*She falls and remains stretched on
the ground.*)

TIME

You would do much better to hope. . . .

247

And now, that is all. . . . (*Consulting his hour-glass.*) We have only sixty-three seconds left. . . .

> (*Last and violent movements among the* CHILDREN *departing and remaining. They exchange hurried farewells.*)

THE BLUE CHILDREN

Good-bye, Pierre! . . . Good-bye, Jean! . . . Have you all you want? . . . Announce my idea! . . . Have you got the new turnscrew? . . . Mind you speak of my melons! . . . Have you forgotten nothing? . . . Try to know me again! . . . I shall find you! . . . Don't lose your ideas! . . . Don't lean too far into space! . . . Send me your news! . . . They say one can't . . . Oh, try, do try! . . . Try to tell us if it's nice! . . . I will come to meet you! . . . I shall be born on a throne! . . .

TIME (*shaking his keys and his scythe*)

Enough! Enough! . . . The anchor's
raised! . . .

> (*The sails of the galley pass and
> disappear. The voices of
> the* CHILDREN *in the galley
> are heard in the distance:*
> "The Earth! The Earth!
> . . . I can see it! . . .
> How beautiful it is! . . .
> How bright it is! . . .
> How big it is!" . . . *Then,
> as though issuing from the
> depths of the abyss, an ex-
> tremely distant song of
> gladness and expectation.*)

TYLTYL (*to* LIGHT)

What is that? . . . It is not they singing.
. . . It sounds like other voices. . . .

LIGHT

Yes, it is the song of the mothers coming
out to meet them. . . .

> (*Meanwhile,* TIME *closes the
> opalescent doors. He turns
> to take a last look at the hall*

The Blue Bird

and suddenly perceives TYL-
TYL, MYTYL and LIGHT.)

TIME (*dumbfoundered and furious*)

What's that? . . . What are you doing
here? . . . Who are you? . . . Why
are you not blue? . . . How did you
get in? . . . (*He comes forward,
threatening them with his scythe.*)

LIGHT (*to* TYLTYL)

Do not answer! . . . I have the Blue Bird.
. . . He is hidden under my cloak.
. . . Let us escape. . . . Turn the
diamond, he will lose our traces. . . .
(*They slip away on the left, between the columns in the
foreground.*)

CURTAIN

ACT VI

Scene i.—The Leave-taking.

*The stage represents a wall with a small
door. It is the break of day.*

(*Enter* Tyltyl, Mytyl, Light, Bread,
Water, Sugar, Fire *and* Milk)

You would never guess where we are. . . .
Tyltyl
Well, no, Light, because I don't know. . . .
Light
Don't you recognise that wall and that
little door? . . .
Tyltyl
It is a red wall and a little green door.
Light
And doesn't that remind you of any‑
thing? . . .
Tyltyl
It reminds me that Time shewed us the
door. . . .

251

LIGHT

How odd people are when they dream.
. . . They do not recognise their own
hands. . . .

TYLTYL

Who is dreaming? . . . Am I? . . .

LIGHT

Perhaps it's myself. . . . Who can tell?
. . . However, this wall contains a
house which you have seen more than
once since you were born. . . .

TYLTYL

A house which I have seen more than once
since I was born? . . .

LIGHT

Why yes, sleepy-head! . . . It is the house
which we left one evening, just a year
ago, to a day. . . .

TYLTYL

Just a year ago? . . . Why, then. . . .

LIGHT

Come, come! . . . Don't open great eyes
like sapphire caves. . . . It's the dear
old house of your father and
mother. . . .

TYLTYL (*going up to the door*)

But I think. . . . Yes, really. . . . It
seems to me. . . . This little door.
. . . I recognise the wooden pin.
. . . Are they in there? . . . Are we
near mummy? . . . I want to go in
at once. . . . I want to kiss her at
once! . . .

LIGHT

One moment. . . . They are sound asleep;
you must not wake them with a start.
. . . Besides, the door will not open
till the hour strikes. . . .

TYLTYL

What hour? . . . Is there long to wait? . . .

LIGHT

Alas, no! . . . A few poor minutes. . . .

TYLTYL

Aren't you glad to be back? . . . What is
it, Light? . . . You are quite pale,
you look ill. . . .

LIGHT

It's nothing, child. . . . I feel a little sad,
because I am leaving you. . . .

253

The Blue Bird

TYLTYL

Leaving us? . . .

LIGHT

I must. . . . I have nothing more to do here; the year is over, the Fairy is coming back to ask you for the Blue Bird. . . .

TYLTYL

But I haven't got the Blue Bird! . . . The one of the Land of Memory turned quite black, the one of the Future turned quite pink, the Night's are dead and I could not catch the one in the Forest. . . . Is it my fault if they change colour, or die, or escape? . . . Will the Fairy be angry and what will she say? . . .

LIGHT

We have done what we could. . . . It seems likely that the Blue Bird does not exist or that he changes colour when he is caged. . . .

TYLTYL

Where is the cage? . . .

BREAD

Here, master. . . . It was entrusted to my
diligent care during our long journey;
to-day, now that my mission is drawing to an end, I restore it to your
hands, untouched and carefully closed,
as I received it. . . . (*Like an orator
making a speech*) And now, in the
name of all, I crave permission to add
a few words. . . .

FIRE

He has not been called upon to speak! . . .

WATER

Order! . . .

BREAD

The malevolent interruptions of a contemp-
tible enemy, of an envious rival. . . .

FIRE

An envious rival! . . . What would you be
without me? . . . A lump of shape-
less and indigestible dough. . . .

WATER

Order! . . .

FIRE

I won't be shouted down by you! . . .

The Blue Bird

*(They threaten each other and
are about to come to blows.)*

LIGHT *(raising her wand)*

Enough! . . .

BREAD

The insults and the ridiculous pretensions
of an element whose notorious misbe-
haviour and whose scandalous ex-
cesses drive the world to despair. . . .

FIRE

You fat pasty-face!

BREAD *(raising his voice)*

Will not prevent me from doing my duty
to the end. . . . I wish, therefore, in
the name of all . . .

FIRE

Not in mine! . . . I have a tongue of my
own! . . .

BREAD

In the name of all and with a restrained
but simple and deep emotion, to take
leave of two distinguished children,
whose exalted mission ends to-day.
. . . When bidding them farewell,

with all the grief and all the fondness
which a mutual esteem. . . .

TYLTYL

What? . . . You are bidding us farewell?
. . . Are you leaving us too? . . .

BREAD

Alas, needs must, since the hour when
men's eyes are to be opened has not yet
come. . . . I am leaving you, it is
true; but the separation will only be
apparent, you will no longer hear me
speak. . . .

FIRE

That will be no loss! . . .

WATER

Order! Silence! . . .

FIRE

I shall keep silence when you cease babbling
in the kettles, the wells, the brooks,
the waterfalls and the taps. . . .

LIGHT (*threatening them with her wand*)

That will do, do you hear? . . . You are
all very quarrelsome; it is the coming
separation that sets your nerves on
edge like this. . . .

BREAD (*with great dignity*)

That does not apply to me. . . . I was
saying, you will no longer hear me
speak, no longer see me in my living
form. . . . Your eyes are about to
close to the invisible life of the
Things; but I shall always be there,
in the bread-pan, on the shelf, on the
table, beside the soup, I who am, if I
may say so, with Water and Fire, the
most faithful companion, the oldest
friend of Man. . . .

FIRE

Well, and what about me? . . .

LIGHT

Come, the minutes are passing, the hour is
at hand which will send us back into
silence. . . . Be quick and kiss the
children. . . .

FIRE (*rushing forward*)

I first! I first! . . . (*Violently kissing the*
CHILDREN.) Good-bye, Tyltyl and
Mytyl! . . . Good-bye, my darlings.
. . . Think of me if ever you want
any one to set fire to anything. . . .

MYTYL

Oh! Oh! . . . He's burning me! . . .

TYLTYL

Oh! Oh! . . . He's scorched my nose! . . .

LIGHT

Come, Fire, moderate your transports.
    . . . Remember you're not in your
chimney. . . .

WATER

What an idiot! . . .

BREAD

What a vulgarian! . . .

FIRE

There, look; I will put my hands in my
    pockets. . . . But don't forget me.
    . . . I am the friend of Man. . . .
    I shall always be there, in the hearth
    and in the oven; and I will come some-
    times and put out my tongue for you
    when you are cold or sad. . . . I
    shall be warm in winter and roast
    chestnuts for you. . . .

WATER (*approaching the* CHILDREN)

I shall kiss you without hurting you, ten-
    derly, my children. . . .

The Blue Bird

FIRE

Take care, you'll get wet! . . .

WATER

I am loving and gentle; I am kind to human
beings. . . .

FIRE

What about those you drown? . . .

WATER

Love the wells, listen to the brooks. . . .
I shall always be there. . . .

FIRE

She has flooded the whole place. . . .

WATER

When you sit down, in the evening, beside
the springs—there is more than one
here in the forest—try to understand
what they are trying to say. . . .

FIRE

Enough! Enough! . . . I can't swim! . . .

WATER

I shall no longer be able to tell you as
clearly as I do to-day that I love you;
but you will not forget that that is
what I am saying to you when you
hear my voice. . . . Alas! . . . I can

say no more. . . . My tears choke me
and prevent my speaking. . . .

FIRE

It doesn't sound like it! . . .

WATER

Think of me when you see the water-bottle.
. . . Alas! I have to be silent there;
but my thoughts will always be of
you. . . . You will find me also in
the ewer, the watering-can, the cistern
and the tap. . . .

MILK (*approaching timidly*)

And me in the milk-jug. . . .

TYLTYL

What, you too, my dear Milk, so shy and
so good? . . . Is everybody
going? . . .

SUGAR (*naturally mawkish and sancti-monious*)

If you have a little corner left in your
memory, remember sometimes that
my presence was sweet to you. . . .
That is all I have to say. . . . Tears
are not in harmony with my tempera-

ment and they hurt me terribly when
they fall on my feet. . . .

BREAD

Jesuit! . . .

FIRE (yelping)

Sugar-plum! Lollipop! Caramel! . . .

TYLTYL

But where are Tylette and Tylô gone to?
. . . What are they doing? . . .

> (The CAT is heard to utter
> shrill cries.)

MYTYL (alarmed)

It's Tylette crying! . . . He is being
hurt! . . .

(Enter the CAT, running, his hair on end
and dishevelled, his clothes torn, holding his handkerchief to his cheek, as
though he had the toothache. He
utters angry groans and is closely
pursued by the DOG, who overwhelms
him with bites, blows and kicks.)

THE DOG (beating the CAT)

There! . . . Have you had enough? . . .

262

Do you want any more? . . . There!
There! There! . . .

LIGHT, TYLTYL *and* MYTYL (*rushing forward to part them*)

Tylô! . . . Are you mad? . . . Well, I
never! . . . Down! . . . Stop that,
will you? . . . How dare you? . . .
Wait, wait! . . .

(*They part the* DOG *and the*
CAT *by main force.*)

LIGHT

What is it? . . . What has happened? . . .

THE CAT (*blubbering and wiping his
eyes*)

It's the Dog, Mrs. Light. . . . He in-
sulted me, he put tin tacks in my food,
he pulled my tail, he beat me; and I
had done nothing, nothing, nothing at
all! . . .

THE DOG (*mimicking him*)

Nothing, nothing, nothing at all! . . .
(*In an undertone, with a mocking
grimace*) Never mind, you've had
some, you've had some and you're going to have some more! . . .

MYTYL (*pressing the* CAT *in her arms*)
My poor Tylette, where has he hurt you?
> . . . Tell me. . . . I shall cry
> too. . . .
> LIGHT (*to the* DOG, *severely*)
Your conduct is all the more unworthy
> since you have chosen for this dis-
> graceful exhibition the already most
> painful moment when we are about to
> part from these poor children. . . .
> THE DOG (*suddenly sobered*)
To part from these poor children? . . .
> LIGHT
Yes; the hour which you know of is at hand.
> . . . We are going to return to si-
> lence. . . . We shall no longer be
> able to speak to them. . . .
THE DOG (*suddenly uttering real howls of
> despair and flinging himself upon the*
> CHILDREN, *whom he loads with vio-
> lent and tumultuous caresses*).
No! No! . . . I refuse! . . . I refuse!
> . . . I shall always talk! . . . You
> will understand me now, will you not,
> my little god? . . . Yes! Yes! Yes!

. . . And we shall tell each other
everything, everything, everything!
. . . And I shall be very good. . . .
And I shall learn to read and write
and play dominoes! . . . And I shall
always be very clean. . . . And I
shall never steal anything in the
kitchen again. . . . Shall I do a wonderful trick for you? . . . Would you
like me to kiss the Cat? . . .

MYTYL (*to the* CAT)

And you, Tylette? . . . Have you nothing
to say to us? . . .

THE CAT (*in an affected and enigmatic
tone*)

I love you both as much as you deserve. . . .

LIGHT

Now let me, in my turn, children, give you
a last kiss. . . .

TYLTYL *and* MYTYL (*hanging on to*
LIGHT'S *dress*)

No, no, no, Light! . . . Stay here with
us! . . . Daddy won't mind. . . .
We will tell mummy how kind you
have been. . . .

LIGHT

Alas! I cannot! . . . This door is closed to
us and I must leave you. . . .

TYLTYL

Where will you go all alone? . . .

LIGHT

Not very far, my children; over there, to
the Land of the Silence of
Things. . . .

TYLTYL

No, no; I won't have you go. . . . We
will go with you. . . . I shall tell
mummy. . . .

LIGHT

Do not cry, my dear little ones. . . . I
have not a voice like Water; I have
only my brightness, which Man does
not understand. . . . But I watch
over him to the end of his days. . . .
Never forget that I am speaking
to you in every spreading moonbeam,
in every twinkling star, in every
dawn that rises, in every lamp that is
lit, in every good and bright thought
of your soul. . . . (*Eight o'clock*

The Blue Bird

strikes behind the wall.) Listen! . . .
The hour is striking! . . . Good-bye!
. . . The door is opening! . . . In
with you, in with you! . . .

> (*She pushes the* CHILDREN
> *through the door, which
> has half-opened and which
> closes again behind them.*
> BREAD *wipes away a fur-
> tive tear,* SUGAR *and* WA-
> TER, *etc., all in tears, flee
> precipitously and disappear
> in the wings to the right and
> left. The* DOG *howls be-
> hind the scenes. The stage
> remains empty for a mo-
> ment and then the scenery
> representing the wall and
> the little door opens in the
> middle and reveals the last
> scene.*)

SCENE 2.—*The Awakening.*

The same setting as in ACT I, *but the objects, the walls and the atmosphere all*

appear incomparably and magically fresher, happier, more smiling. The daylight penetrates gaily through the chinks of the closed shutters. To the right, at the back, Tyltyl *and* Mytyl *lie sound asleep in their little beds. The* Dog, *the* Cat *and the* Things *are in the places which they occupied in* Act I, *before the arrival of the* Fairy.

Enter Mummy Tyl

Mummy Tyl (*in a cheerfully scolding voice*)

Up, come, get up, you little lazybones! . . . Aren't you ashamed of yourselves? . . . It has struck eight and the sun is high above the trees! . . . Lord, how they sleep, how they sleep! . . . (*She leans over and kisses the* Children.) They are quite rosy. . . . Tyltyl smells of lavender and Mytyl of lilies-of-the-valley. . . . (*Kissing them again*)

268

What sweet things children are! . ....
Still, they can't go on sleeping till mid-
day. . . . I mustn't let them grow
up idle. . . . And, besides, I have
heard that it's not very healthy. . . .
(*Gently shaking* TYLTYL) Wake up,
wake up, Tyltyl. . . .

TYLTYL (*waking up*)

What? . . . Light? . . . Where is she?
. . . No, no, don't go away. . . .

MUMMY TYL

Light? . . . Why, of course it's light
. . . Has been for ever so long. . . .
It's as bright as noonday, though the
shutters are closed. . . . Wait a bit
till I open them. . . . (*She pushes
back the shutters and the dazzling
daylight invades the room.*) There!
See! . . . What's the matter with
you? . . . You look quite blinded. . . .

TYLTYL (*rubbing his eyes*)

Mummy, mummy! . . . It's you! . . .

MUMMY TYL

Why, of course, it's I. . . . Who did you
think it was? . . .

TYLTYL

It's you. . . . Yes, yes, it's you! . . .

MUMMY TYL

Yes, yes, it's I. . . . I haven't changed my
face since last night. . . . Why do you
stare at me in that wonderstruck way?
. . . Is my nose turned upside down,
by any chance? . . .

TYLTYL

Oh, how nice it is to see you again! . . .
It's so long, so long ago! . . . I must
kiss you at once. . . . Again! Again!
Again! . . . And how comfortable
my bed is! . . . I am back at
home! . . .

MUMMY TYL

What's the matter? . . . Why don't you
wake up? . . . Don't tell me you're
ill. . . . Let me see, show me your
tongue. . . . Come, get up and
dress. . . .

TYLTYL

Hullo, I've got my shirt on! . . .

MUMMY TYL

Of course you have. . . . Put on your

breeches and your little jacket. . . .
There they are, on the chair. . . .

TYLTYL

Is that what I did on the journey? . . .

MUMMY TYL

What journey? . . .

TYLTYL

Why, last year. . . .

MUMMY TYL

Last year? . . .

TYLTYL

Why, yes! . . . At Christmas, when I went
away. . . .

MUMMY TYL

When you went away? . . . You haven't
left the room. . . . I put you to bed
last night, and here you are this morning. . . . Have you dreamed all
that? . . .

TYLTYL

But you don't understand! . . . It was last
year, when I went away with Mytyl,
the Fairy, Light—how nice Light is!
—Bread, Sugar, Water, Fire: they
did nothing but quarrel! . . . You're

not angry with me? . . . Did you feel very sad? . . . And what did daddy say? . . . I could not refuse . . . I left a note to explain. . . .

MUMMY TYL

What are you talking about? . . . For sure, either you're ill or else you're still asleep. . . . (*She gives him a friendly shake.*) There, wake up. . . . There, is that better? . . .

TYLTYL

But, mummy, I assure you. . . . It's you that's still asleep. . . .

MUMMY TYL

What! Still asleep, am I? . . . Why, I've been up since six o'clock. . . . I've finished all the cleaning and lit the fire. . . .

TYLTYL

But ask Mytyl if it's not true. . . . Oh, we have had such adventures! . . .

MUMMY TYL

Why Mytyl? . . . What do you mean? . . .

The Blue Bird

TYLTYL

She was with me. . . . We saw grandad
and granny. . . .

MUMMY TYL (*more and more bewildered*)

Grandad and granny? . . .

TYLTYL

Yes, in the Land of Memory. . . . It was
on our way. . . . They are dead, but
they are quite well. . . . Granny
made us a lovely plum-tart. . . . And
then the little brothers—Robert, Jean
and his top—and Madeleine and Pier-
rette and Pauline and Riquette,
too. . . .

MYTYL

Riquette still goes about on all fours! . . .

TYLTYL

And Pauline still has a pimple on her
nose. . . .

MUMMY TYL

Have you found the key of the cupboard
where daddy hides his brandy
bottle? . . .

The Blue Bird

TYLTYL

Does daddy hide a brandy bottle? . . .

MUMMY TYL

Certainly. One has to hide everything when
one has little meddlesome good-for-
nothings like you. . . . But come, out
with it, confess that you took it. . . .
I would rather it was that. . . . I
sha'n't tell daddy. . . . I sha'n't beat
you. . . .

TYLTYL

But, mummy, I don't know where it is. . . .

MUMMY TYL

Just walk in front of me, so that I may see
if you can walk straight. . . .
(TYLTYL *does so*) No, it's not that.
. . . Dear heaven, what is the matter
with them? . . . I shall lose them
too, as I lost the others! . . . (*Suddenly mad with alarm, she calls out*)
Daddy Tyl! . . . Come, quick! The
children are ill! . . .

(*Enter* DADDY TYL, *very calmly, with an
axe in his hand.*)

274

The Blue Bird

DADDY TYL

What is it? . . .

TYLTYL *and* MYTYL (*running up gaily to kiss their father*)

Hullo, daddy! . . . It's daddy! . . . Good-morning, daddy! . . . Have you had plenty of work this year? . . .

DADDY TYL

Well, what's the matter? . . . They don't look ill; they look very well. . . .

MUMMY TYL (*weeping*)

You can't trust their looks. . . . It will be as with the others. . . . They looked quite well also to the end; and then God took them. . . . I don't know what's the matter with them. . . . I put them to bed quite quietly last night; and this morning, when they woke up, everything was wrong. . . . They don't know what they're saying; they talk about a journey. . . . They have seen Light and grandad and granny, who are dead, but who are quite well. . . .

TYLTYL

But grandad still has his wooden leg. . . .

MYTYL

And granny her rheumatics. . . .

MUMMY TYL

Do you hear? . . . Run and fetch the
doctor! . . .

DADDY TYL

Why, no, no. . . . They are not dead yet.
. . . Come, let us look into this. . . .
(*A knock at the front door.*) Come
in! . . .

(*Enter* NEIGHBOUR BERLINGOT, *a little
old woman resembling the* FAIRY *in*
ACT I *and leaning on a stick.*)

THE NEIGHBOUR

Good-morning and a Merry Christmas to
you all! . . .

TYLTYL

It's the Fairy Bérylune! . . .

THE NEIGHBOUR

I have come to ask for a bit of fire for my
Christmas stew. . . . It's very chilly

this morning. . . . Good-morning,
children, how are you? . . .

TYLTYL

Fairy Bérylune, I could not find the Blue
Bird. . . .

THE NEIGHBOUR

What is he saying? . . .

MUMMY TYL

Don't ask me, Madame Berlingot. . . .
They don't know what they are saying.
. . . They have been like that since
they woke up. . . . They must have
eaten something that wasn't good. . . .

THE NEIGHBOUR

Why, Tyltyl, don't you remember Goody
Berlingot, your Neighbour Berlingot? . . .

TYLTYL

Why, yes, ma'am. . . . You are the Fairy
Bérylune. . . . You're not angry with
us? . . .

THE NEIGHBOUR

Béry . . . what? Goodness gracious
me! . . .

The Blue Bird

TYLTYL

Bérylune.

THE NEIGHBOUR

Berlingot, you mean Berlingot. . . .

TYLTYL

Bérylune or Berlingot, as you please,
ma'am. . . . But Mytyl knows. . . .

MUMMY TYL

That's the worst of it, that Mytyl also. . . .

DADDY TYL

Pooh, pooh! . . . That will soon go; I will
give them a smack or two. . . .

THE NEIGHBOUR

Don't; it's not worth while. . . . I know
all about it; it's only a little fit of
dreaming. . . . They must have slept
in the moonbeams. . . . My little girl,
who is very ill, is often like that. . . .

MUMMY TYL

By the way, how is your little girl? . . .

THE NEIGHBOUR

Only so-so. . . . She can't get up. . . .
The doctor says that it's her nerves.
. . . I know what would cure her,
for all that. She was asking me for it

278

only this morning, for her Christmas
box; it's a notion she has . . .

MUMMY TYL

Yes, I know; it's Tyltyl's bird. . . . Well,
Tyltyl, aren't you going to give it at
last to that poor little thing? . . .

TYLTYL

What, mummy? . . .

MUMMY TYL

Your bird. . . . It's no use to you. . . .
You don't even look at it now. . . .
And she has been dying to have it for
ever so long! . . .

TYLTYL

Hullo, that's true, my bird! . . . Where
is he? . . . Oh, there's the cage! . . .
Mytyl, do you see the cage? . . .
It's the one which Bread carried. . . .
Yes, yes, it's the same one, but there's
only one bird in it. . . . Has he eaten
the other, I wonder? . . . Hullo,
why, he's blue! . . . But it's my
turtle-dove! . . . But he's much
bluer than when I went away! . . .
Why, that's the blue bird we were look-

ing for! . . . We went so far and he
was here all the time! . . . Oh, but
it's wonderful! . . . Mytyl, do you
see the bird? What would Light say?
. . . I will take down the cage. . . .
(*He climbs on a chair and takes down
the cage and carries it to the* NEIGH-
BOUR.) There, Madame Berlingot,
there you are. . . . He's not quite
blue yet, but that will come, you shall
see! . . . Take him off quick to your
little girl. . . .

THE NEIGHBOUR

Really? . . . Do you mean it? . . . Do
you give it me like that, straight away
and for nothing? . . . Lord, how
happy she will be! . . . (*Kissing*
TYLTYL) I must give you a kiss! . . .
I fly! . . . I fly! . . .

TYLTYL

Yes, yes; be quick. . . . Some of them
change their colour. . . .

THE NEIGHBOUR

I will come back to tell you what she
says. . . .

280

The Blue Bird

(She goes out.)

TYLTYL (*after taking a long look around him*)

Daddy, mummy, what have you done to the house? . . . It's just as it was, but it's much prettier. . . .

DADDY TYL

How do you mean, it's prettier? . . .

TYLTYL

Why, yes, everything has been painted and made to look new, everything is clean and polished. . . . It was not like that last year. . . .

DADDY TYL

Last year? . . .

TYLTYL (*going to the window*)

And look at the forest! . . . How big and fine it is! . . . One would think it was new! . . . How happy I feel here! . . . (*Going to the bread-pan and opening it*) Where's Bread? . . . I say, the loaves are very quiet. . . . And then here's Tylô! . . . Hullo, Tylô, Tylô! . . . Ah, you had a

271

fine fight! . . . Do you remember, in the forest? . . .

MYTYL

And Tylette. . . . He knows me, but he has stopped talking. . . .

TYLTYL

Mr. Bread. . . . (*Feeling his forehead*) Hullo, the diamond's gone! . . . Who's taken my little green hat? . . . Never mind; I don't want it any more. . . . Ah, Fire! . . . He's a good one! . . . He crackles and laughs to make Water angry. . . . (*Running to the tap*) And Water? . . . Good-morning, Water! . . . What does she say? . . . She still talks, but I don't understand her as well as I did. . . .

MYTYL

I don't see Sugar. . . .

TYLTYL

Lord, how happy I am, happy, happy, happy! . . .

MYTYL

So am I, so am I! . . .

The Blue Bird

MUMMY TYL

What are you spinning round for like that? . . . .

DADDY TYL

Don't mind them and don't distress yourself. . . . They are playing at being happy. . . .

TYLTYL

I liked Light best of all. . . . Where's her lamp? . . . Can we light it? . . . (*Looking round him again.*) Goodness me, how lovely it all is and how glad I feel! . . .

MUMMY TYL

Why? . . .

TYLTYL

I don't know, mummy. . . .

(*A knock at the front-door.*)

DADDY TYL

Come in, come in! . . .

(*Enter the* NEIGHBOUR, *holding by the hand a little girl of a fair and wonderful beauty, who carries* TYLTYL's *dove pressed in her arms.*)

283

THE NEIGHBOUR

Do you see the miracle? . . .

MUMMY TYL

Impossible! . . . Can she walk? . . .

THE NEIGHBOUR

Can she walk? . . . She can run, she can
dance, she can fly! . . . When she
saw the bird, she jumped, just like
that, with one bound, to the window,
to see by the light if it was really
Tyltyl's dove. . . . And then,
whoosh! . . . Out into the street,
like an angel! . . . It was as much as
I could do to keep pace with her. . . .

TYLTYL (*going up to her, wonderstruck*)

Oh, how like Light she is! . . .

MYTYL

She is much smaller. . . .

TYLTYL

Yes, indeed! . . . But she will grow
bigger. . . .

THE NEIGHBOUR

What are they saying? . . . Haven't they
got over it yet? . . .

The Blue Bird

MUMMY TYL

They are better, they are mending. . . . It
will be all right when they have had
their breakfasts. . . .

THE NEIGHBOUR (*pushing the* LITTLE
GIRL *into* TYLTYL'S *arms*).

Come along, child, come and thank Tyltyl. . . .

> (TYLTYL, *suddenly frightened,
> takes a step back.*)

MUMMY TYL

Well, Tyltyl, what's the matter? . . .
Are you afraid of the little girl? . . .
Come, give her a kiss, a good big
kiss. . . . No, a better one than that.
. . . You're not so shy as a rule! . . .
Another one! . . . But what's the
matter with you? . . . You look as if
you were going to cry. . . .

> (TYLTYL, *after kissing the*
> LITTLE GIRL *rather awk-
> wardly, stands before her
> for a moment and the two
> children look at each other
> without speaking; then*

285

TYLTYL *strokes the dove's head*.)

TYLTYL

Is he blue enough? . . .

THE LITTLE GIRL

Yes, I am so pleased with him. . . .

TYLTYL

I have seen bluer ones. . . . But those
which are quite blue, you know, do
what you will, you can't catch
them. . . .

THE LITTLE GIRL

That doesn't matter; he's lovely. . . ..

TYLTYL

Has he had anything to eat? . . .

THE LITTLE GIRL

Not yet. . . . What does he eat? . . .

TYLTYL

Anything: corn, bread, Indian corn, grass-
hoppers. . . .

THE LITTLE GIRL

How does he eat, say? . . .

TYLTYL

With his beak. You'll see, I will show
you. . . .

286

The Blue Bird

> (*He moves in order to take the
> bird from the* LITTLE
> GIRL'S *hands. She resists
> instinctively; and, taking ad-
> vantage of the hesitation of
> their movements, the* DOVE
> *escapes and flies away.*)

THE LITTLE GIRL (*with a cry of despair*)
Mother! . . . He is gone! . . . (*She
bursts into sobs.*)

TYLTYL

Never mind. . . . Don't cry. . . . I will
catch him again. . . . (*Stepping to
the front of the stage and addressing
the audience.*) If any of you should
find him, would you be so very kind
as to give him back to us? . . . We
need him for our happiness, later
on. . . .

CURTAIN